C O N T E N T S

Congratulations. You are studying to take the GED Tests in order to earn your high school equivalency certificate.

Since there is a lot of ground to cover in preparing for the test, we thought that we could help you by developing this *GED Skill* workbook series. The formula for GED success is as simple as *1–2–3.*

1. Evaluate, pages 1–13

In school and in your GED class, you have studied much of what you need to know to pass the GED. You may be asking yourself, *What do I already know? What do I need to learn? What do the GED questions look like?*

In Part 1 of this book, you will take an inventory that will help you figure out where you are in your studies. After you check your answers, you will use the *Diagnostic Chart* to target your efforts so that you can work most effectively to pass the test.

Some of the questions will check your skills; some will determine your abilities with the types of questions that you will encounter on the actual GED. In Parts 2 and 3, you will have a chance to review and practice what you need to know to pass the test.

2. Review, pages 14–53

Once you have taken the inventory, you can decide which topics you need to review. You may want to select lessons based on the *Diagnostic Chart and Study Planner* or work through the entire section of the book.

Part 2 of this book consists of 20 social studies lessons. Each lesson has two parts:

- Skill Review
- Skill Practice

3. Practice, pages 54–85

Once you feel that you have covered the skills, the next step is to practice answering the types of questions that you will find on the GED Tests.

Part 3 of this book consists of *GED Skill Builder* lessons. These eight lessons will review the types of questions that you will see on the actual test. These lessons have three parts:

- Sample Question and Think It Through
- Guided Practice
- GED Practice

Be sure that you use the hints in this part of the book. They will help you to think like a successful GED test-taker.

Best of luck,
The GED Skill Workbook Team

GED
Skill Workbook Series

Social Studies

New Readers Press

GED® Skill Workbook: Social Studies
ISBN 978-1-56420-516-2

Distributed by:
New Readers Press
ProLiteracy's Publishing Division
104 Marcellus Street, Syracuse, New York 13204
www.newreaderspress.com

Printed in the United States of America
10   9   8   7   6

Proceeds from the sale of New Readers Press materials support professional development, training, and technical assistance programs of ProLiteracy that benefit local literacy programs in the U.S. and around the globe.

GED® is a registered trademark of the American Council on Education and may not be used without permission. The GED® and GED Testing Service® brands are administered by GED Testing Service LLC under license.

GED® Skill Workbook Team
Project Developer: Caren Van Slyke
Writer: Marion Castellucci
Editor: Elizabeth Kaplan
Copy Editor: Liz Stout
Production: Jean Farley Brown
Art and Design: Karen Blanchard
Cover Design: Kimbrly Koennecke

Evaluation

Directions

On the following pages you will find passages and graphics similar to those on the GED Social Studies Test.

Read each passage carefully and then answer the questions that follow. Some questions will be based on a passage, some will be based on a graphic, and some will be based on both a passage and a graphic. You may copy and use the answer sheet below, or you may write your answers on another sheet of paper.

When you have finished with the test, check your answers on page 12. Then use the *Diagnostic Chart and Study Planner* on page 13 to help you decide which areas you need to work on the most in this book.

1. ① ② ③ ④ ⑤
2. ① ② ③ ④ ⑤
3. ① ② ③ ④ ⑤
4. ① ② ③ ④ ⑤
5. ① ② ③ ④ ⑤
6. ① ② ③ ④ ⑤
7. ① ② ③ ④ ⑤
8. ① ② ③ ④ ⑤
9. ① ② ③ ④ ⑤
10. ① ② ③ ④ ⑤
11. ① ② ③ ④ ⑤

12. ① ② ③ ④ ⑤
13. ① ② ③ ④ ⑤
14. ① ② ③ ④ ⑤
15. ① ② ③ ④ ⑤
16. ① ② ③ ④ ⑤
17. ① ② ③ ④ ⑤
18. ① ② ③ ④ ⑤
19. ① ② ③ ④ ⑤
20. ① ② ③ ④ ⑤
21. ① ② ③ ④ ⑤
22. ① ② ③ ④ ⑤

23. ① ② ③ ④ ⑤
24. ① ② ③ ④ ⑤
25. ① ② ③ ④ ⑤
26. ① ② ③ ④ ⑤
27. ① ② ③ ④ ⑤
28. ① ② ③ ④ ⑤
29. ① ② ③ ④ ⑤
30. ① ② ③ ④ ⑤
31. ① ② ③ ④ ⑤
32. ① ② ③ ④ ⑤
33. ① ② ③ ④ ⑤

34. ① ② ③ ④ ⑤
35. ① ② ③ ④ ⑤
36. ① ② ③ ④ ⑤
37. ① ② ③ ④ ⑤
38. ① ② ③ ④ ⑤
39. ① ② ③ ④ ⑤
40. ① ② ③ ④ ⑤
41. ① ② ③ ④ ⑤
42. ① ② ③ ④ ⑤

World History

Questions 1 and 2 refer to this information and diagram.

In the 1500s, European exploration of the Americas led to a huge geographic redistribution of organisms, as shown in this diagram.

The Columbian Exchange

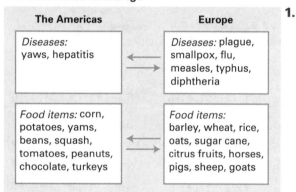

1.

Which food did Europe get from the Americas?

(1) barley
(2) corn
(3) oats
(4) rice
(5) sugar cane

2. Farm animals the Europeans brought to the Americas adapted so well that many ran wild. For example, the eight pigs that Columbus released in the Greater Antilles in 1493 reproduced very rapidly. Over time, they stripped areas of vegetation, causing topsoil erosion. Given this negative environmental impact, why did Europeans continue to bring their farm animals to the Americas?

(1) Europeans valued the animals because they prevented the spread of disease.
(2) Europeans valued the animals because they could be released into the wild.
(3) Europeans valued the animals because they fed on native vegetation.
(4) Europeans valued the animals because they could be sold to the Indians.
(5) Europeans valued familiar foods more than the environment.

Questions 3 and 4 refer to this information and map.

Between 1405 and 1423, Ming Emperor Yunglo sent out seven voyages of exploration. The first fleet consisted of 62 ships with 28,000 crew members and diplomats. These expeditions brought back "barbarians" and exotic animals like giraffes. Many in the Chinese court thought the voyages were a waste of money better spent on defense. After Yunglo's death, the voyages stopped.

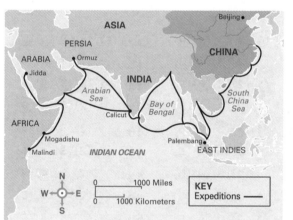

3.

According to the map, which of the following was the farthest place from China that these expeditions reached?

(1) the Bay of Bengal
(2) Calicut, India
(3) the East Indies
(4) Malindi, in Africa
(5) Ormuz, in Persia

4. Which of the following is most similar in scope to these early Chinese explorations?

(1) the Dutch fur trading ventures up and down the Hudson River
(2) the French exploration of the Mississippi River Valley
(3) the English settlement of Jamestown on the James River
(4) the early Portuguese voyages from Europe, around Africa, to Asia
(5) the European commerce on the Rhine River

Questions 5 and 6 refer to this time line and quote.

The Cold War

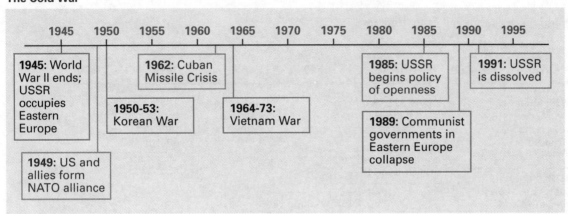

In 1947, U.S. President Harry Truman stated: "I believe that it must be the policy of the United States to support free peoples who are resisting attempted subjugation by armed minorities or by outside pressures." By "outside pressures" Truman meant the Union of Soviet Socialist Republics (USSR). For more than 40 years, the United States and the Soviet Union waged the Cold War to influence politics around the world.

5. Soon after Truman stated his doctrine, what did the United States do to strengthen its ability to contain Soviet communism?

   (1) established NATO
   (2) fought the Korean War
   (3) fought the Vietnam War
   (4) helped win World War II
   (5) resolved the Cuban Missile Crisis

6. What was the ultimate result of the events at the end of this time line?

   (1) The USSR became a superpower.
   (2) NATO was dismantled.
   (3) Communism spread throughout the world.
   (4) Europe became more powerful.
   (5) The Cold War ended because the USSR collapsed.

7. In 336 B.C., Alexander the Great inherited the kingdoms of Macedonia and Greece. In 334, he raised a large army and marched east into Asia Minor, defeating the Persians there. He then marched south and west into Egypt, where he founded Alexandria at the mouth of the Nile. The city was ideally located to link Greece, Asia Minor, and Egypt. Alexander then resumed his eastward march and conquered Persia. Not content, Alexander marched farther east into India. There his soldiers mutinied. They had marched 11,000 miles since leaving Greece. Alexander withdrew to Persia, where he died in 323 B.C., having created the largest empire the world had ever seen.

Which of the following is the best summary of this passage?

   (1) Alexander the Great inherited the kingdoms of Greece and Macedonia.
   (2) Alexander founded the city of Alexandria to control the eastern Mediterranean.
   (3) In just over 10 years, Alexander the Great conquered an empire stretching from Greece to Egypt to India.
   (4) Alexander's armies marched farther than 11,000 miles in the course of conquering foreign lands.
   (5) Alexander the Great died in Persia, after returning from India with his rebellious army.

U.S. History

Questions 8 and 9 refer to the following time line.

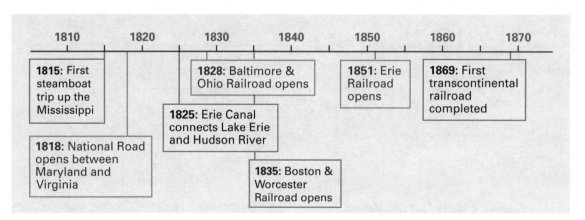

8. In which year did the Erie Canal open?

(1) 1810
(2) 1815
(3) 1828
(4) 1825
(5) 1851

9. Which is the best title for this time line?

(1) American Economic Growth, 1810–1870
(2) The Industrial Revolution
(3) U.S. Transportation, 1810-1870
(4) The Beginnings of Railroads in America
(5) The Rise and Decline of the Steamboat

10. In 1794, a group of farmers in western Pennsylvania refused to pay a federal excise tax on whiskey. Instead, they attacked the U.S. tax collectors. Concerned about this challenge to the new U.S. government, President Washington called up the state militia and put down the rebellion.

Which of the following actions was also a threat to federal authority?

(1) the purchase of Louisiana in 1803
(2) the transport of freed slaves to Liberia from 1822 to 1860
(3) the secession of South Carolina from the Union in 1860
(4) Congress's passage of the Sherman Anti-Trust Act in 1890
(5) federal prohibition of the manufacture or sale of alcohol in 1919

11. In *Common Sense* (1776), Thomas Paine wrote: Small islands not capable of protecting themselves are the proper objects for kingdoms to take under their care; but there is something very absurd in supposing a continent to be perpetually ruled by an island. In no instance hath nature made the satellite larger than its . . . planet; and . . . England and America, with respect to each other, reverse the common order of nature . . .

What assumption is Paine making but not stating?

(1) Every region has a right to self-rule.
(2) Political power is naturally proportional to size.
(3) A nation must have a strong military.
(4) England and America are equals.
(5) England is a satellite of America.

Questions 12 and 13 refer to this World War II poster.

12. Who does the standing man represent?

(1) a U.S. soldier
(2) a Congressman
(3) an ordinary American citizen
(4) a local politician
(5) a trial witness

13. How does this poster try to persuade people to buy war bonds?

(1) by showing an assembly of citizens who had the freedom to oppose the war
(2) by depicting a group of men who would soon become soldiers
(3) by showing people listening to their leader with respect
(4) by implying that people of all incomes can afford to buy war bonds
(5) by showing that the U.S. was fighting for a freedom that Americans value

Questions 14–16 refer to the following map.

Eastern North America, 1650

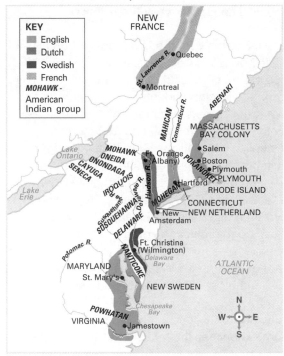

14. What area did the Dutch control?

(1) the St. Lawrence River Valley
(2) the Hudson River Valley
(3) the Massachusetts Bay area
(4) the Delaware Bay area
(5) the Chesapeake Bay area

15. Who lived closest to the Potomac River?

(1) the English   **(4)** the Swedes
(2) the Dutch   **(5)** the Abenaki
(3) the French

16. Which question can be answered by the information on the map?

(1) Which of the English settlements was established earliest?
(2) When did the Dutch and the Swedes lose control of their colonies?
(3) Which settlement had the greatest population?
(4) Which settlements were mainly commercial?
(5) Which American Indian group lived in the Jamestown area?

Civics and Government

Questions 17 and 18 refer to this passage.

Article I, Section 8, of the U.S. Constitution lists 17 specific powers of Congress. In order, they include the power to: (1) tax, (2) borrow money, (3) regulate foreign and interstate commerce, (4) set rules for naturalization and bankruptcies, (5) coin money, (6) punish counterfeiters, (7) establish post offices, (8) protect copyrights, (9) establish lower federal courts, (10) punish piracy and offenses against international law, (11) declare war, (12) raise armies, (13) maintain a navy, (14) make rules for the armed services, (15) call up the militia to enforce national laws, (16) make rules for the militia, and (17) govern the seat of government (Washington, D.C.), military bases, and other government buildings.

Finally, Section 8 concludes with what has become known as the "elastic clause." This clause grants Congress the power to *make all Laws which shall be necessary and proper for carrying into Execution the foregoing Powers. . .*

17. What is suggested by the elastic clause at the end of Section 8?

(1) The legislative branch is the least powerful branch of government.
(2) The framers of the Constitution wanted to place strict limits on Congress.
(3) Congress can take over the executive and judicial branches if needed.
(4) Congress can make laws related to the 17 powers explicitly granted.
(5) Congress can increase its powers simply by passing any law.

18. Which is an example of Congress using its third power plus the elastic clause?

(1) setting a federal minimum wage
(2) closing selected naval bases
(3) instituting a draft
(4) setting a tax on stock dividends
(5) setting immigration quotas

Questions 19 and 20 refer to this graph.

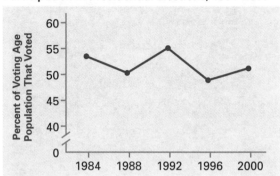

Participation in Presidential Elections, 1984–2000

Source: Congressional Quarterly

19. Approximately what percentage of the voting age population voted in the 1988 presidential election?

(1) 40%
(2) 45%
(3) 50%
(4) 55%
(5) 60%

20. The voting age population shown in the graph above includes everyone over 18. However, many people over 18 are not eligible to vote. For example, noncitizens and many felons cannot vote. If these people were not counted in the pool of voters, then voter turnout rates would decrease.

Is this conclusion correct?

(1) Yes. The total voter pool would become smaller, and the percent of people voting would also become smaller.
(2) Yes. The total voter pool would become larger, and the percent of people voting would become smaller.
(3) No. The total voter pool would become larger, and the percent of people voting would become smaller.
(4) No. The total voter pool would become smaller, and the percent of people voting would become larger.
(5) No. Excluding noncitizens and felons from the total voter pool would have no effect on the percent of people voting.

In a democracy, the role of the news media is to provide information to citizens, debate issues, and keep an eye on the performance of government officials. The First Amendment of the Constitution protects this role by guaranteeing freedom of the press.

NEWS ORGANIZATION CHART

EDITOR IN-CHIEF

MANAGING EDITOR

CITY DESK   METRO DESK   FOREIGN DESK   NATIONAL DESK

J-LO BUREAU   BRITNEY BUREAU   SCOTT PETERSON BUREAU

ANNA NICOLE SMITH BUREAU   MICHAEL JACKSON BUREAU   JANET JACKSON BUREAU

ROBERT BLAKE BUREAU

MARLETTE© 2004
TALLAHASSEE DEMOCRAT
dougmarlette.com

21. What is being shown in this cartoon?

(1) the table of contents of a newspaper
(2) a chart showing today's news, features, and personalities
(3) a chart showing who is responsible for reporting different types of news
(4) a table of organization for an agency that oversees the news media
(5) a table of organization for the Constitution and its amendments

22. Which of the following is likely to be an opinion of the cartoonist, rather than a fact?

(1) One role of the press in a democracy is to keep citizens informed about government.
(2) Different departments of a news organization cover different types of news.
(3) The First Amendment of the Constitution protects freedom of the press.
(4) An editor-in-chief is in charge of all departments in a news organization.
(5) The news media are doing a poor job of reporting on real news issues.

A politician who already holds an elective office is called an incumbent. In an election, the incumbent has a built-in advantage over his or her opponents. An incumbent can do mass mailings to constituents, often speaks at local events, and has easy access to the news media. These advantages are called the incumbency effect.

23. Which of these people could take advantage of the incumbency effect in an election?

(1) a member of the House of Representatives running for reelection
(2) a judge who has just been appointed to the federal court of appeals
(3) a political newcomer running for office for the first time
(4) a Republican running for a Senate seat held by a Democrat
(5) a politician who resigns before completing the term because of a corruption scandal

Economics

Questions 24–26 refer to the following section of a state income tax return form.

State Schedule V Checkoff Contributions

Note: Contributions reduce your refund or increase your balance due.

		$1
1.	Olympic Contribution	☐
2.	Organ Transplant Fund	☐
3.	Council on the Arts	☐
4.	Childhood Disease Victims' Fund	☐
5.	Military Family Relief Fund	☐

6. TOTAL CONTRIBUTIONS - add lines 1, 2, 3, 4, 5.
Enter here and on page 1, line 16. ☐

24. What is the most likely reason a group like the Organ Transplant Fund would want to be listed in this section of an income tax return?

   (1) It's a way to be linked to other good causes in the state.
   (2) It's a way to reduce the balance due.
   (3) It's a way to ask for contributions from all taxpayers in the state.
   (4) The group could make a contribution.
   (5) The group would get a tax refund.

25. If a filer checks a box, how much money will go to the fund indicated?

   (1) $1
   (2) $5
   (3) $10
   (4) no money
   (5) The fund will owe taxes.

26. Which part of this form provides evidence that contributions will be added to the amount of tax the taxpayer owes?

   (1) the title
   (2) the note
   (3) the total contributions line
   (4) the list of funds
   (5) the checkoff boxes

Questions 27–29 refer to the following bar graph.

American Workers with Access to Selected Employee Benefits, 2003

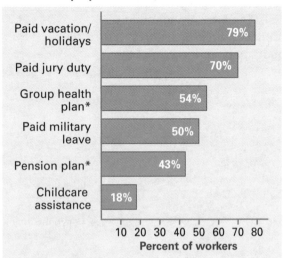

*2001 data
Source: U.S. Bureau of Labor Statistics

27. What percentage of workers can get help with childcare from their employer?

   (1) 70%   **(4)** 43%
   (2) 54%   **(5)** 18%
   (3) 50%

28. Which employee benefit is the most common among American workers?

   (1) pension plan
   (2) paid jury duty
   (3) paid vacations and holidays
   (4) health plan
   (5) paid military leave

29. Which of the following conclusions is supported by data in the graph?

   (1) Most American workers spend their vacation time off at home.
   (2) Most American workers travel during their vacation time off.
   (3) American workers get more holidays than vacation days off.
   (4) American workers get more vacation days than holidays off.
   (5) Some American workers are not paid for time off for vacations and holidays.

Questions 30–32 refer to the following information and editorial cartoon.

In this cartoon, the Democratic Party is represented by a donkey, and the Republican Party, by an elephant. When this cartoon was published in 2003, there was a Republican president and the Republicans controlled Congress.

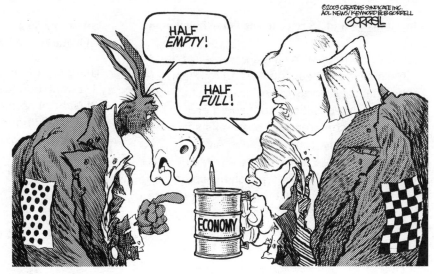

By permission of Bob Gorrell and Creators Syndicate, Inc.

30. Why is the elephant holding the cup?

(1) The Republican Party is selling pencils.
(2) The Democratic Party wants campaign contributions.
(3) The Republican Party wants campaign contributions.
(4) The Republican Party controls economic policy.
(5) The Democratic Party wants to lower taxes.

31. What do the patches represent?

(1) hard times
(2) wealth
(3) old-fashioned values
(4) stylishness
(5) the economy

32. How do the two parties' views of the economy compare?

(1) Both think the economy is doing well.
(2) Both think the economy is doing poorly.
(3) The Democrats think the economy is doing poorly, and the Republicans think it is doing well.
(4) The Democrats think the economy is doing well, and the Republicans think it is doing poorly.
(5) The Democrats think the economy should be stimulated, and the Republicans think it should be slowed.

33. Economists classify unemployment as frictional, structural, or cyclical. People who are frictionally unemployed are briefly between jobs or just entering or reentering the job market. People who are structurally unemployed are out of work for a long time and cannot find a similar job. People who are cyclically unemployed are jobless because of a general downturn in the economy.

Which person is structurally unemployed?

(1) a homemaker reentering the workforce after taking twenty years off to raise children
(2) a recent graduate who has been looking for a full-time job for a month
(3) a steel worker who was let go two years ago because the plant shut down
(4) an auto worker who was laid off for two months because demand for cars was sluggish
(5) a worker who quit a job to go to college full time

Geography

Questions 34 and 35 refer to the following passage.

Nomadic herders, also called pastoralists, tend animals such as sheep, goats, and reindeer. They move with their flocks to find fresh pastures. In 2005, the United Nations sponsored an international conference of pastoralists from 23 countries, mostly from Africa and Asia.

The pastoralists discussed problems common to their way of life, such as educating their children, who are always on the move, and keeping milk from spoiling. All agreed that the most serious problem they face is the loss of grazing land through the spread of farms, ranches, and private development, including the building of homes, shopping malls, and office parks. In Spain, nomadic migratory routes are protected by law, even when they go through a big city. However, this nomad-friendly policy is the exception. Most nations that try to help pastoralists deal with the loss of grazing land have programs to settle them in fixed locations and turn them into ranchers.

34. What is a key characteristic of pastoral life?

    (1) scattered settlements
    (2) hardy crops
    (3) urban development
    (4) movement from place to place
    (5) government-protected routes

35. How would a pastoralist and a private developer be likely to view the use of land?

    (1) They would both favor limiting access to land.
    (2) They would both favor free public access to all land.
    (3) They would both favor developing land for residential and commercial use.
    (4) A pastoralist would favor private ownership of land, and a developer would favor public access to land.
    (5) A pastoralist would favor public access to land, and a developer would favor private ownership of land.

Questions 36 and 37 refer to the following information and map.

There are three types of political boundaries:
(1) Ethnic boundaries follow settlement patterns.
(2) Natural boundaries follow landscape features.
(3) Artificial boundaries are often based on lines of latitude or longitude.

36. Of the following sets, which includes states that all border New Mexico?

    (1) Arizona, Missouri, Colorado, Texas
    (2) Arizona, Colorado, Oklahoma, Texas
    (3) Arkansas, Kansas, Louisiana, Utah
    (4) Arkansas, Louisiana, Oklahoma, Utah
    (5) Kansas, Oklahoma, Texas, Utah

37. How should the eastern half of Oklahoma's boundary with Texas be classified?

    (1) as natural, because it follows a river
    (2) as natural, because it follows a mountain range
    (3) as artificial, because it follows a line of longitude
    (4) as artificial, because it follows a line of latitude
    (5) as ethnic, because it separates Oklahomans from Texans

Questions 38–40 refer to the following table.

Top U.S. Mineral* Producers, 2003

Rank	State	Value
1	California	$3,170,000,000
2	Nevada	$2,940,000,000
3	Arizona	$2,100,000,000
4	Texas	$2,030,000,000
5	Florida	$2,000,000,000

*Does not include fuel
Source: U.S. Geological Survey

38. According to the table, what was the value of minerals produced in Florida in 2003?

(1) $2,000 million
(2) $2,030 million
(3) $2,100 million
(4) $2,940 million
(5) $3,170 million

39. Which state ranked third in non-fuel mineral production?

(1) Arizona
(2) California
(3) Florida
(4) Nevada
(5) Texas

40. Which of the following best restates the data provided about California?

(1) In 2003, California produced over $3 billion in minerals.
(2) California produced more minerals in 2003 than Nevada, Arizona, Texas, and Florida.
(3) California outranked all other mineral-producing states.
(4) California was the top-producing state with over $3 billion in minerals in 2003.
(5) California was the top fuel-producing state in 2003.

41. A renewable resource is something people use that will not run out. Which of the following is a renewable resource?

(1) oil   **(4)** coal
(2) natural gas   **(5)** wind
(3) iron ore

Question 42 refers to the following photograph.

© Roger Ressmeyer/CORBIS

42. Whose point of view is supported by the photograph above?

(1) a factory safety worker proud of the work he is doing
(2) an environmentalist favoring stricter standards for waste disposal
(3) a tank manufacturer promoting the quality of its storage tanks
(4) a barrel manufacturer promoting the quality of its waste barrels
(5) an electric company promoting energy conservation efforts

Answers and explanations start on page 12.

1. **(2) corn** Look in the section of the diagram that lists American foods introduced to Europe.

2. **(5) Europeans valued familiar foods more than the environment.** European farm animals provided food and a reminder of home. In addition, there was so much land in the Americas that when the vegetation in one area was destroyed, the settlers could move on to new places.

3. **(4) Malindi, in Africa** Of the choices, the map shows that this trading city on the east coast of Africa was farthest from China.

4. **(4) the early Portuguese voyages from Europe, around Africa, to Asia** Both the Chinese and Portuguese expeditions were ocean voyages to distant continents.

5. **(1) established NATO** Truman's speech was in 1947; the NATO alliance was established in 1949.

6. **(5) The Cold War ended because the USSR collapsed.** The time line shows that by 1991 the Soviet Union had fallen apart. The Cold War ended as a result.

7. **(3) In just over 10 years, Alexander the Great conquered an empire stretching from Greece to Egypt to India.** This statement best summarizes the main points of the passage.

8. **(4) 1825** The time line indicates that the Erie Canal opened in 1825.

9. **(3) U.S. Transportation, 1810–1870** The time line shows advances in steamboats, canals, and railroads in this period.

10. **(3) the secession of South Carolina from the Union in 1860** South Carolina was the first state to leave the Union, which was a great threat to federal authority.

11. **(2) Political power is naturally proportional to size.** Paine's argument that a continent shouldn't be ruled by a small island depends on the view that political authority is related to the size of a region.

12. **(3) an ordinary American citizen** Note the work clothes and hat. This man looks like an average American of the time.

13. **(5) by showing that the U.S. was fighting for a freedom that Americans value** The poster appeals to the patriotic feelings aroused by the freedoms that Americans value.

14. **(2) the Hudson River Valley** Check the key to see how the Dutch settlements are represented on the map. Then locate the region where the Dutch settled.

15. **(1) the English** Locate the Potomac River on the map. Then use the key to identify which group lived closest to that river.

16. **(5) Which American Indian group lived in the Jamestown area?** The map shows where local tribes lived. The Powhatan lived near Jamestown.

17. **(4) Congress can make laws related to the 17 powers explicitly granted.** The elastic clause stretches Congress's powers only with respect to the 17 explicitly granted powers.

18. **(1) setting a federal minimum wage** As part of its power to regulate interstate commerce, Congress sets the federal minimum wage.

19. **(3) 50%** Find the point on the trend line that represents 1988. Then read across to the vertical axis.

20. **(4) No. The total voter pool would become smaller, and the percent of people voting would become larger.** If the total pool of voters gets smaller, then the number of voters will be a larger portion of it.

21. **(3) a chart showing who is responsible for reporting different types of news** This is a table of organization for a newspaper or other news-gathering company.

22. **(5) The news media are doing a poor job of reporting on real news issues.** The cartoonist indicates that the national reporters are busy covering pop stars rather than political issues and events.

23. **(1) a member of the House of Representatives running for reelection** This person can take advantage of the incumbency effect because he or she is already a member of the House.

24. **(3) It's a way to ask for contributions from all taxpayers in the state.** The state tax return goes to every household. From the organization's point of view, this is free fund-raising.

25. **(1) $1** The dollar amount is indicated above the column of boxes.

26. **(2) the note** The note indicates that any contributions will be added to tax owed or deducted from a tax refund.

27. **(5) 18%** The bar graph shows that 18% of workers have access to assistance with childcare.

28. **(3) paid vacations and holidays** The bar graph shows that 79% of American workers get paid for vacation and holiday time off; this is the highest percentage for all employee benefits.

29. **(5) Some American workers are not paid for time off for vacations and holidays.** The graph shows that a majority of workers are paid when they take vacation and holiday time. That means there are some who are not paid.

30. **(4) The Republican Party controls economic policy.** By making the elephant (the Republican) hold the cup (the economy), the cartoonist is suggesting that the party in power (through a Congressional majority and control of the White House) controls the economy.

31. **(1) hard times** Patches usually represent impoverishment. The ragged state of the clothes confirms this interpretation.

32. **(3) The Democrats think the economy is doing poorly, and the Republicans think it is doing well.** The Democrat sees the cup as half empty and the Republican sees it as half full, indicating their respective viewpoints.

33. **(3) a steel worker who was let go two years ago because the plant shut down** This person is structurally unemployed because the industry has changed and there are no longer jobs that require the skills he or she has.

34. **(4) movement from place to place** Pastoral life is nomadic—people lead their animals from place to place to find food for them.

35. **(5) A pastoralist would favor public access to land, and a developer would favor private ownership of land.** That's because pastoralists are not concerned with owning property but with grazing animals on land when necessary. In contrast, private developers want to use land to build houses, shops, factories, and so on; with land ownership, developers have the most control over what is built and they have clear rights to income from rental or sale of the properties they build.

36. **(2) Arizona, Colorado, Oklahoma, Texas** The map shows that these four states have boundaries with New Mexico.

37. **(1) as natural, because it follows a river** The eastern half of Oklahoma's border with Texas is the Red River.

38. **(1)$2,000 million** Find the row for Florida; then find the value of Florida's mineral production, in the third column.

39. **(1) Arizona** Scan down the first column for the state ranked third. Read across to the middle column to find the state; it is Arizona.

40. **(4) California was the top-producing state with over $3 billion in minerals in 2003.** This is the choice that restates all the California data.

41. **(5) wind** Wind is a resource that never runs out.

42. **(2) an environmentalist favoring stricter standards for waste disposal** An environmentalist could use the waste-strewn scene in this photo as evidence that higher standards are needed to prevent land pollution.

Diagnostic Charts and Study Planner

1. Check your answers to the Social Studies Skills Inventory on pages 12 and 13.
2. Circle the numbers of the questions you got correct.
3. Add the number of questions that you got right for each content area skill (across), and write the number under Total Correct.
4. Add the number of total questions that you got correct (down).
5. Check off (✓) the skill areas that you feel you most need to work on.
   Note: Question numbers appear in both the Content Review chart and GED Skill chart. Circle the questions you got right in both charts.

QUESTION NUMBERS	TOTAL CORRECT	CONTENT REVIEW	✓	PAGE NUMBERS
1, 2, 3, 4, 5, 6, 7	_____/7	World History		pp. 14–23
8, 9, 10, 11, 12, 13, 14, 15, 16	_____/9	U.S. History		pp. 24–33
17, 18, 19, 20, 21, 22, 23	_____/7	Civics and Government		pp. 34–41
24, 25, 26, 27, 28, 29, 30, 31, 32, 33	_____/10	Economics		pp. 42–47
34, 35, 36, 37, 38, 39, 40, 41, 42	_____/9	Geography		pp. 48–53
TOTAL	_____ **/ 42**			

QUESTION NUMBERS	TOTAL CORRECT	GED SKILL	✓	PAGE NUMBERS
		Thinking Skills		
7, 9, 17, 28, 34, 40	_____/6	Comprehension		pp. 54–57
4, 10, 18, 23, 33, 37, 41	_____/7	Application		pp. 58–61
6, 11, 13, 22, 24, 32, 35	_____/7	Analysis		pp. 62–65
2, 16, 20, 26, 29, 42	_____/6	Evaluation		pp. 66–69
		Graphic Skills		
1, 19, 27, 38, 39	_____/5	Graphs and Charts		pp. 70–73
12, 21, 30, 31	_____/4	Editorial Cartoons and Photos		pp. 74–77
5, 8, 25	_____/3	Time Lines and Diagrams		pp. 78–81
3, 14, 15, 36	_____/4	Maps		pp. 82–85
TOTAL	_____ **/ 42**			

Skill Review

River Valley Civilizations

Early civilizations were located in river valleys, which provided fertile soil, water for drinking and irrigation, and easy transportation.

- Ancient Egypt developed in the Nile River Valley of North Africa starting about 5000 B.C. The Nile flooded each year, depositing rich soil for farming. The Egyptians used a picture-based system of writing called hieroglyphics, developed geometry and astronomy, and built the Great Pyramids.

- Mesopotamia grew in the valley between the Tigris and Euphrates rivers (present-day Iraq), beginning about 4500 B.C. It was ruled by a succession of peoples including Sumerians, Akkadians, Babylonians, Hittites, Assyrians, and Persians. Key accomplishments included cuneiform writing and Hammurabi's code of law—the first law code to apply to an entire empire.

- The Indus River Valley civilization arose in northwestern India around 2500 B.C. Its two major cities, Harappa and Mohenjo-Daro, were large, planned communities. Cotton cloth was an important export. The civilization was in decline by 1500 B.C. Around the same time, Aryan tribes invaded from the northwest. Hinduism developed from the religious practices that the Aryans brought.

- Ancient China developed in the Yellow River Valley by 1700 B.C. with the rise of the Shang dynasty (royal family). The Chinese developed a picture-based writing system still in use today. They were the first to produce silk. They also were skilled bronze workers and makers of pottery. Under the Zhou dynasty, a feudal system of government arose, with warring lords under the Zhou emperor.

Classical Civilizations

The civilizations of ancient Greece and Rome provided the foundation for Western science, philosophy, law, and government.

- Ancient Greece consisted of many small city-states on the coast of the Aegean Sea; it later spread to other parts of the Mediterranean and eastward to the Indus River Valley under Alexander the Great around 325 B.C. In Athens, the political system shifted to democratic rule by about 800 B.C. Citizenship was reserved for free men of Athenian descent—a small portion of the population. But these citizens participated directly in the governing assembly. They each had a vote in the proceedings. During the fourth and fifth century B.C., Greek artists produced great works, including plays and sculpture. Greek philosophers emphasized the power of reason in their study of the natural world.

- Ancient Rome was centered on the Tiber River in Italy. In 509 B.C., the Romans established a republic, in which citizens elected leaders to represent them. The Roman republic lasted just under 500 years, during which Rome conquered the Mediterranean world. In 27 B.C., Augustus became the first emperor, ending the republic. The Pax Romana, a period of peace, began then and lasted until A.D.180.

World History Practice 1

Choose the **one best answer** to each question.

1. According to the passage, which civilization was the original producer of silk?

   (1) Egypt
   (2) Mesopotamia
   (3) the Indus River Valley
   (4) China
   (5) Rome

2. Which civilization arose in the area between the Tigris and Euphrates rivers?

   (1) Egypt
   (2) Mesopotamia
   (3) China
   (4) Greece
   (5) Rome

3. Which civilization developed a form of government in which citizens elected officials to represent them?

   (1) Egypt
   (2) Mesopotamia
   (3) the Indus River Valley
   (4) Athens
   (5) the Roman republic

4. Some small American towns hold town meetings in which all citizens can participate, making decisions about town budgets and other civic matters. To which of the following is this most similar?

   (1) Hammurabi's code of law
   (2) the feudal system of the Zhou dynasty
   (3) the Athenian assembly
   (4) the Roman republic
   (5) the Pax Romana

5. In 44 B.C., Rome began to grant Roman citizenship to the elite in conquered provinces outside Italy. What was the likely result of this practice?

   (1) revolt of the provinces against Rome
   (2) greater unity in the Roman Empire
   (3) corruption in provincial government
   (4) peace among the conquered peoples
   (5) civil war in the provinces

6. The code of Hammurabi contained 282 laws governing trade, family, personal property, and other areas of life. Typically, the punishment for a crime fit the crime. For example, if a building collapsed and killed those inside, the builder was put to death.

   Which saying summarizes a Mesopotamian value reflected in the code of Hammurabi?

   (1) It takes a thief to catch a thief.
   (2) To err is human, to forgive, divine.
   (3) Live and let live.
   (4) A man's home is his castle.
   (5) An eye for an eye; a tooth for a tooth.

Question 7 refers to the following map.

Some Early Civilizations in the Americas

7. Which civilization did the Spanish encounter when they arrived in Mexico in the early 1500s?

   (1) the Olmec civilization
   (2) the Mayan civilization
   (3) the Toltec civilization
   (4) the Aztec civilization
   (5) the Incan civilization

Answers and explanations start on page 86.

Feudalism in Western Europe

From about 500 A.D, when the Western Roman Empire collapsed, Europe became a battleground for Germanic and Slavic tribes. The knowledge and accomplishments of ancient Greece and Rome were largely forgotten, and trade and travel became difficult. In this environment, feudal societies arose. Feudalism was characterized by local rule of lords who pledged loyalty to a relatively weak king. The lords held large tracts of land, which they divided among their vassals, or lesser lords. In turn, the lesser lords divided their portions among their knights—the mounted, armored warriors. The majority of the population was made up of peasants, who farmed the land under the protection of the lords. Warfare was common. Castles were built throughout Europe to protect the lords' lands.

The Roman Catholic Church was the major unifying influence in Western Europe from 500 to about 1350. The Church expanded its power by converting thousands of people and establishing its own government, laws, courts, and system of taxation. The Church controlled vast amounts of land and wealth, and its officials were also often feudal lords.

Byzantium and the Rise of Islam

Unlike the Western Roman Empire, which collapsed because of barbarian invasions, the Eastern Roman Empire survived into the 1400s. Called the Byzantine Empire, its capital was Constantinople (Istanbul in present-day Turkey), and it ruled the eastern Mediterranean. Power was centralized in the emperor, who had efficient government bureaucrats to run the empire and a well-trained army for its defense.

Byzantium was attacked by both Western Europe, during the Crusades, and armies of the Islamic Empire. The religion of Islam was founded by Muhammad in Saudi Arabia in 622. From 622 to 750, Islam spread north and west into Palestine, Syria, North Africa, and Spain. To the north and east, it expanded into Persia and India.

At its peak, the Islamic Empire made important advances in medicine, mathematics, and science. These ideas eventually made their way into Western Europe, where intellectual activity had stagnated during the Middle Ages.

African Civilizations

During this same period, civilizations based on trade in gold and salt developed in West Africa. The kingdom of Ghana (700 to 1000) was the first of these. At its height around 900, Ghana was a wealthy center of trade based on gold. Ghana declined just before 1100. Mali, to the southeast of Ghana, became the next important African empire. It arose around 1200. Some rulers of Mali converted to Islam. Their capital city, Timbuktu, became a center of learning in the Islamic world. In the 1400s, the Songhai took over Mali, established a new empire, and ruled until about 1600.

World History Practice 2

Choose the one best answer to each question.

1. Which civilization gave rise to Timbuktu as a center of learning?

   (1) Ghana
   (2) Mali
   (3) Songhai
   (4) Byzantium
   (5) Western Europe

2. According to the passage, what was the main difference in the way Western Europe and Byzantium were governed during the Middle Ages?

   (1) Western Europe had decentralized government by feudal lords, and Byzantium had centralized authority in an emperor.
   (2) Western Europe had representative government, and Byzantium had a direct democracy.
   (3) Western Europe was ruled by nonreligious emperors, and Byzantium was ruled by the Catholic Church.
   (4) Western Europe was governed by knights and Byzantium, by bureaucrats.
   (5) Western Europe was governed by Muslim emperors and Byzantium, by feudal lords.

3. Feudalism often arises where there is no tradition of self-government and no strong central authority, and where war is common. In the year 2004, which of the following nations exhibited feudal characteristics?

   (1) Iraq, which was ruled by a central interim government
   (2) Swaziland, which was ruled by a king who appointed a portion of the legislature
   (3) Japan, which had a constitutional monarchy and an elected legislature
   (4) Afghanistan, where large areas of the countryside were controlled by warlords
   (5) Finland, which was governed by multi-party coalitions in its legislature

4. In addition to the Catholic Church's laws, governing bodies, and taxes, which factor was most likely to contribute to the Church's unifying influence across Europe?

   (1) It commissioned art for its churches.
   (2) It engaged in power struggles with European kings.
   (3) Its monks copied manuscripts.
   (4) Its theologians wrote works of philosophy.
   (5) Its officials and priests all spoke Latin.

Question 5 refers to the following information and chart.

The Crusades were undertaken by the Catholic Church, which sought to recapture Jerusalem and the Holy Land from the Muslims. Major Crusades are summarized here.

Crusade	Important events
First Crusade, 1096	Captured Jerusalem from the Turks. Muslims retook Jerusalem in 1187.
Third Crusade, 1189	Richard the Lion-Hearted of England negotiated access to Jerusalem for Christian pilgrims.
Fourth Crusade, 1202	Knights captured the Byzantine city of Constantinople, ignoring the Holy Land.
Children's Crusade, 1212	Many children sold into slavery by merchants in Marseilles, France.

5. Which question about the Crusades can be answered by the information in the chart?

   (1) Why did knights volunteer?
   (2) What weapons were used?
   (3) In which Crusade were the stated goals of the Church best met?
   (4) Which Crusade involved the largest number of troops?
   (5) Which Crusade had the greatest number of losses?

Answers and explanations start on page 86.

The Renaissance, 1350–1600

The Renaissance was not an event, but an age of rebirth for Europe. It began around 1350 in the city-states of northern Italy, which had become rich from trade in the Mediterranean. With wealth came the time and money to support scholarly and artistic pursuits. Scholars studied the humanities and recovered knowledge from the ancient Greeks and Romans. Artists such as da Vinci and Michelangelo revived the classical principles of Greek and Roman art, emphasizing realism and balance. From Italy, the Renaissance spread to France and northern Europe. The spread of ideas was helped by the invention of the printing press in 1455. For the first time, books could be printed in great numbers at fairly low cost.

The Reformation, 1517–1600

Along with the revival of scholarship and the arts came calls for reform of the Catholic Church. The Church had become a worldly, wealthy organization. To finance its bureaucracy, building projects, and wars, Renaissance popes increased the fees charged for baptism, marriage, and funerals. They permitted the sale of indulgences—pardons of sins. In 1517, a German monk, Martin Luther, attacked the sale of indulgences and challenged the Church in other ways. He presented his ideas in a work called the 95 Theses. In it, Luther emphasized the importance of faith for salvation and the importance of the Bible in Christian worship. He stressed the role of the individual, rather than of priests, in religious life. Luther's 95 Theses were printed, and his ideas spread across Europe. Many Germans supported Luther. By the time of Luther's death in 1546, about half the princes in Germany had become Protestants (those who protested).

The Protestant Reformation spread from Germany to Scandinavia, Switzerland, and England. There King Henry VIII cut ties to Rome and established the Church of England, with himself as its head. In addition, the Protestant Reformation spurred the Catholic Reformation—a movement to change the Catholic Church from within and to fight the spread of Protestantism. After the Catholic Reformation, Protestants gained few new followers in Europe. Protestant sects thrived in England, Scotland, Scandinavia, and northern Germany. Catholics were the majority in Italy, France, Spain, Ireland, and southern Germany.

Exploration and Colonization, 1450–1750

In the 1400s and 1500s, Europeans started venturing beyond the Mediterranean and the Atlantic coast. The Portuguese sailed along the African coast and up through the Indian Ocean to India to trade for spices. Columbus, looking for a shorter route to India and China, found the Americas instead. These early voyages of trade and exploration led to the founding of European colonies. Portugal and Spain colonized Central and South America, while Spain, the Netherlands, Sweden, France, and England founded colonies in North America. Many colonists brought slaves from Africa to work their farm fields. Europeans, Africans, and Native Americans contributed to the development of the Americas.

World History Practice 3

Choose the <u>one best answer</u> to each question.

1. Which of the following was a goal of the Catholic Reformation?

   (1) to end the architectural projects of the Church
   (2) to eliminate priests from religious life
   (3) to improve the Church from inside the organization
   (4) to adopt the 95 Theses of Martin Luther
   (5) to increase the sale of indulgences

2. As implied by the passage, what were the earliest European explorers looking for?

   (1) good trade routes to the Orient
   (2) good land for agriculture
   (3) people to colonize
   (4) scientific data about the oceans
   (5) maps of the world

3. Which Church practice was Martin Luther challenging with his thesis that faith, not any acts a person could perform, leads to the forgiveness of sins?

   (1) the reverence granted to the pope
   (2) the living quarters given to priests
   (3) the fees charged for baptism and other ceremonies
   (4) the selling of indulgences
   (5) the wars conducted by the Church

4. Which invention has been as important in spreading ideas in today's world as the printing press was in the Renaissance?

   (1) books   **(4)** photocopiers
   (2) newspapers   **(5)** the Internet
   (3) the automobile

5. Reread the last paragraph of the passage. Whose point of view does the paragraph most strongly reflect?

   (1) Portuguese navigators
   (2) Indian spice traders
   (3) Native American rulers
   (4) enslaved Africans
   (5) European colonizers

<u>Question 6</u> refers to the following information and painting.

In the 1500s, an Italian monk painted this map of Venice, whose symbol is the lion. The Latin scroll tells of the city's wealth and glories.

Scala/Art Resource, NY

6. What is the most likely reason that the leaders of Venice commissioned this work?

   (1) to provide an aid to ships approaching the city
   (2) to promote the image of Venice and attract business
   (3) to encourage travel to Asia
   (4) to promote the sale of ships
   (5) to provide a street map for residents

Answers and explanations start on page 86.

The Scientific Revolution and the Enlightenment

During the 1500s and 1600s, new inventions such as the microscope and telescope improved scientists' ability to observe the natural world. They began to rely on observation, experiments, and mathematics to build scientific knowledge. Some of the new theories were revolutionary. For example, the idea that Earth was the center of the universe had been accepted by the Catholic Church for hundreds of years. But astronomers such as Copernicus, Kepler, and Galileo published strong evidence that Earth revolved around the sun. Galileo was put on trial by the Church for his views, found guilty, and sentenced to house arrest for the rest of his life. Still, the new view of Earth's place in the universe was gradually accepted.

As people realized that observation, reason, and mathematics could help decode the laws of nature, they also applied these processes to human society. Philosophers of the Enlightenment, as the late 1600s and 1700s were known, used reason to discover the laws of human behavior. An English philosopher, John Locke, was particularly influential. He believed that all people had natural rights, including the rights to life, liberty, and property. He also thought that government was a contract between the ruler and the ruled, and that rulers could stay in power only as long as they had the consent of their subjects. These ideas helped spur political revolutions in the British American colonies and in France.

Political Revolutions in America and France

From 1400 to about 1700, the monarchies of Europe grew strong, and the divine right of kings to govern was widely accepted. But near the end of this period, the political ideas of the Enlightenment gave people a new way to think about government, especially when they were dissatisfied with it. For example, in the Declaration of Independence, the American colonists justified their revolution by showing that King George III of England had broken the contract between the ruler and the ruled. A few years later in France, attempts to reform the monarchy and the feudalistic system failed. The French Revolution began in 1789 and eventually led to the rise of Napoleon, who instituted democratic reforms even while crowning himself emperor.

The Industrial Revolution

In addition to the political revolutions of this period, the Industrial Revolution brought great changes in the way people worked and lived. The Industrial Revolution began in Great Britain around 1750 and spread to Europe and North America in the early 1800s. Increased population led to increased demand for goods such as cloth, which had been hand woven in people's homes. New inventions used waterpower to speed up the spinning of yarn and the weaving of textiles. These machines were housed in factories, which were built near rivers to tap the power of water. People began to work in the factories rather than at home to produce goods. Later, the steam engine, coal power, and improved transportation further revolutionized the manufacture and distribution of goods. As a result, people left their farms and migrated to cities to work.

World History Practice 4

Choose the <u>one best answer</u> to each question.

1. According to the passage, what was the Enlightenment?

(1) the discovery that Earth was not the center of the universe as had previously been believed

(2) a period in the 1600s and 1700s in which observation and reason were applied to the study of human societies

(3) the use of new technologies such as microscopes and telescopes to observe nature

(4) the belief in the divine right of kings and the absolute power of the monarch

(5) the overthrow of governments by citizens who felt the contract between ruler and ruled had been broken

2. What does the passage imply about the effect of the Industrial Revolution on employment?

(1) The number of farm workers increased during this period.

(2) The number of people who were self-employed increased during this period.

(3) Employment shifted from farms and homes to factories and cities.

(4) Unemployment grew in the cities as more people moved there.

(5) The number of factory workers decreased during this period.

3. What assumption was held by most people who believed that Earth was the center of the universe?

(1) The universe exists to provide a place for human beings.

(2) Human beings evolved on Earth by chance.

(3) Human beings are just one species among many.

(4) New scientific theories should be embraced by the Catholic Church.

(5) Observation and experiment are the best methods for furthering knowledge of the universe.

4. Which of the following provides an example of an Enlightenment idea—that all people have a natural right to liberty—being put into practice?

(1) the divine right of kings
(2) taxation without representation
(3) the rise of the middle class
(4) the abolition of slavery
(5) the establishment of labor unions

<u>Question 5</u> refers to the following graph.

Per Person Annual Income in Great Britain, 1700–1860

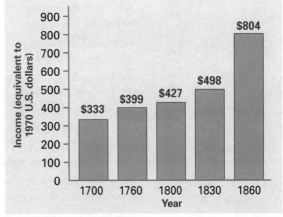

Source: Estimates by N.F.R. Crafts

5. What evidence in the graph best supports the conclusion that the standard of living rose significantly in Great Britain during the Industrial Revolution?

(1) Per person annual income was $333 in 1700.

(2) Per person annual income increased between 1700 and 1760.

(3) Per person annual income rose by only $28 between 1760 and 1800.

(4) Per person annual income increased slowly until 1800.

(5) Per person annual income doubled between 1760 and 1860.

Answers and explanations start on page 86.

The Age of Imperialism

By the late 1800s, a rise in prosperity, due to the Industrial Revolution, had strengthened the European nations. Nationalism was also on the rise in Europe. European countries began to compete with one another for resources and markets. To satisfy their needs, European nations took control of Africa (except for Liberia and Ethiopia), and areas of Asia. The United States extended its imperial reach to the Caribbean, Latin America, and the Philippines. The period from 1870 to 1914 is often called the Age of Imperialism.

Imperialism refers to the domination of one country over the political, economic, or cultural life of another.

The World Wars

By the early 1900s, nationalism had become a powerful force in Europe. Some nations, like Great Britain and France, had been unified for centuries and had stable societies. Other countries were less stable. They were home to ethnic groups that sought independence. In addition, conflicts over colonies contributed to tensions in Europe. There was a buildup of military power and alliances throughout the continent. In 1914, the assassination of Archduke Franz Ferdinand of Austria-Hungary by a Serb led to the outbreak of World War I. Austria-Hungary, Germany, and the Ottoman Empire were the Central Powers; on the other side of the conflict, Britain, France, and Russia were the Allied Powers. In 1917, the United States entered the war on the side of the Allied Powers, and by the end of 1918, the war was over. The Allies had won.

The Treaty of Versailles ended World War I. It set harsh terms for the Central Powers, in particular for Germany, which had to pay reparations, or damages, for the war. Economic hard times in the postwar period, especially the Great Depression, contributed to continuing political problems. Totalitarian governments became established in Russia (communism), Germany (Nazism), Italy (fascism), and Japan (militarism). In 1939, Germany invaded Poland, sparking a war that quickly engulfed the world. From 1939 until 1945, Germany, Italy, and Japan (the Axis Powers) fought Great Britain, and eventually Russia and the United States (the Allied Powers). World War II ended in an Allied victory, but not before the United Stated dropped atomic bombs on the cities of Hiroshima and Nagasaki in Japan.

The Spread of Democracy

After World War II, independence movements among the European colonies grew strong in Africa and Asia. The two new superpowers—the United States and the Soviet Union—supported the independence movements. The United States supported the establishment of democratic, capitalist nations, and the Soviet Union supported communist governments. Newly independent nations fell under the influence of one or the other superpower. Eventually, with the fall of the Soviet Union in 1991, many nations in the Soviet bloc took steps to establish democratic governments and free market economies.

Choose the <u>one best answer</u> to each question.

1. According to the passage, which of these regions were under U.S. imperial control?

   (1) large parts of Asia
   (2) Africa except for Liberia and Ethiopia
   (3) the Caribbean, Central America, and the Philippines
   (4) the Soviet Union and Japan
   (5) Hiroshima and Nagasaki

2. One form of imperialism was a sphere of influence, in which the imperial nation claimed exclusive investment and trading privileges, while the local government controlled other matters. Which of the following was a sphere of influence?

   (1) The British took over the government of South Africa from the Boers, descendants of Dutch colonists.
   (2) Great Britain controlled trading rights in the Yangtze River Valley and at the port of Shanghai in China.
   (3) Great Britain established a colonial government in India that ruled over all regions of the country.
   (4) Belgium colonized the region of the Congo River, ruling the area and exploiting its natural resources.
   (5) France set up a colonial government in Indochina as a stepping-stone to southern China.

3. Which event set off World War II?

   (1) the German invasion of Poland
   (2) the assassination of Archduke Ferdinand
   (3) the alliance of the United States with Great Britain
   (4) the bombing of two Japanese cities
   (5) the Treaty of Versailles

4. Which of these nations fought on the side of Germany in World War II?

   (1) Italy
   (2) Holland
   (3) France
   (4) the United States
   (5) Great Britain

5. Which is the most likely reason that both the United States and the Soviet Union supported the colonial independence movements?

   (1) Both nations sought to govern the newly independent nations.
   (2) Both nations sought to retaliate against their World War II allies.
   (3) Both nations thought that the European empires were governed justly.
   (4) Both nations saw an opportunity to gain influence and allies worldwide.
   (5) Both nations valued the spread of democracy and free markets.

<u>Question 6</u> refers to the following British cartoon, which appeared after World War I.

PASSING THE BUCK.

6. Which detail of the cartoon indicates that the cartoonist believed the Allied Powers would be paid little, if any, money in war damages?

   (1) Each leader wears a different hat.
   (2) Each Allied leader writes "Pay up."
   (3) The German leader writes "I'm broke."
   (4) Uncle Sam is wearing the tallest hat.
   (5) Uncle Sam is at the end of the line.

Answers and explanations start on page 86.

Spanish Conquests

From 1492 to 1550, Spain conquered the following regions: all of South America except Brazil; the Caribbean, Central America, and Mexico; and the southern part of North America, from Florida to California. Spanish settlers sent gold, silver, wood, and sugar back to Spain. They imported African slaves, finished goods, and more colonists to the New World. As a result, Spain became the richest and most powerful nation on Earth. Also as a result, the native populations of these regions were decimated by infectious diseases brought by the Spanish, as well as by forced labor in Spanish mines.

French and Dutch Colonies

In the early 1600s, the French established their first permanent settlement in the Americas, in Canada. The first French Canadians were fur traders, who concentrated their outposts along the St. Lawrence River. This gave them access to the Great Lakes and to the Mississippi River. France did not encourage settlement, so the population of their outposts remained small. To the south, the Dutch established New Netherlands along the Hudson River, in present-day New York. From there, they carried on fur trading with the Iroquois.

English Colonies

In the mid-1600s, the Dutch were driven out by the English, who had established colonies to the north and south of them in New England and Virginia. The English renamed the former Dutch colony New York. In addition to New York, the English established other colonies on the east coast of North America. These included the following settlements.

- Jamestown, Virginia Established by the Virginia Company in 1607, Jamestown's settlers grew tobacco. In 1619, Jamestown established the House of Burgesses, the first representative assembly in America.
- Plymouth, Massachusetts In 1620, the *Mayflower* brought Pilgrims to New England. Most were religious dissidents who had broken from the Church of England. One notable feature of the colony was the Mayflower Compact, a document signed by the settlers before they landed. A simple constitution, it pledged them to abide by majority rule and stated the powers and duties of the government.
- Massachusetts Bay Colony In 1630, a group of about 1,000 Puritans settled in Boston. Within a few years, many more Puritans came and established other towns in Massachusetts Bay Colony. In this colony, all free men who were members of the Puritan church elected a representative assembly, which chose the governor.
- Maryland In 1632, Lord Baltimore established a colony in Maryland. His goal was to provide a haven for fellow Catholics, as well as obtain great wealth for himself and the king. Maryland granted religious freedom to all Christians.
- Rhode Island Banished from Massachusetts because of his religious views, Roger Williams founded Providence in 1636. The colony recognized the rights of Native Americans and provided religious freedom for Catholics, Quakers, and Jews, as well as Protestants.

U.S. History Practice 1

Choose the <u>one best answer</u> to each question.

1. According to the passage, which nation was the wealthiest in the early 1500s?

(1) Spain
(2) Portugal
(3) the Netherlands
(4) France
(5) England

2. What was the main purpose of French settlements in North America?

(1) converting Indians to Christianity
(2) gold mining
(3) farming
(4) fur trading
(5) establishing religious freedom

3. William Penn, a Quaker, founded the colony of Pennsylvania, in part to establish a place for Quakers to live and worship freely. Based on the passage, to which colony is this most similar?

(1) French outposts on the St. Lawrence
(2) New Netherlands
(3) New York
(4) Jamestown
(5) Maryland

4. Which of the following did several of the English colonies described in the passage have in common?

(1) democratic political institutions
(2) religious freedom for everyone
(3) economies based on gold and sugar
(4) economies based on tobacco
(5) large numbers of non-English settlers

5. On the marshy coast of the Carolina colony, deadly diseases like malaria and yellow fever spread. What was a likely effect?

(1) Rice plantations spread inland.
(2) Conflict arose among colonists, slaves, and Indians.
(3) The population grew slowly.
(4) The economy was based on health care.
(5) Slaves outnumbered Europeans.

6. Which of the following was likely to have been an assumption of the men who signed the Mayflower Compact?

(1) Signing would make them wealthy.
(2) The king's authority was absolute.
(3) A society needs rules to prosper.
(4) The richest among them would lead.
(5) Their stay in Plymouth was temporary.

<u>Questions 7 and 8</u> refer to this paragraph and chart.

African slavery took hold first in South America and the West Indies during the early 1500s. The chart gives the number of enslaved persons brought to the Americas from Africa over three centuries.

Where Enslaved Africans Were Taken, 1526–1810

Place	Number of Slaves
Brazil	3,647,000
Spanish South America	746,000
West Indies	4,040,000
Mexico/Central America	224,000
British North America	427,000

Source: Estimates by Phillip D. Curtin, *The Atlantic Slave Trade*

7. About how many slaves were brought to Spanish South America?

(1) 224,000   **(4)** 3,650,000
(2) 427,000   **(5)** 4,040,000
(3) 746,000

8. Which question can be answered by the information in the paragraph and the chart?

(1) What part of Africa did most slaves come from?
(2) To which region in the Americas were most slaves brought?
(3) What was the population of African slaves in North America in 1700?
(4) How many slaves died en route to the Americas from 1500 to 1810?
(5) Did the African slave trade end in 1810?

Answers and explanations start on page 86.

Conflict Between Great Britain and the Colonies

For more than a hundred years, Great Britain left the American colonies to govern themselves and to pursue their own economic interests. However, in the mid-1700s, Britain, with help from the American colonists, won French Canada in the French and Indian War. It began to maintain a larger army in North America and to collect taxes to pay for the war. In the Proclamation of 1763, Britain forbade colonists to move west of the Appalachians. This was the first of several actions by the British that were resisted by the colonists. For example, the Stamp Act of 1765 required colonists to buy stamps for almost all printed items, including newspapers and legal documents. The Townshend Acts of 1767 taxed imports of tea, glass, and paper.

The colonists reacted by boycotting British goods, which eventually led to the repeal of both acts. Colonists continued to express anger when taxes and other laws were levied without their input. Their protests began to get violent. For example, in 1773 in the Boston Tea Party, a cargo of British tea was dumped in the harbor. The British government retaliated with several acts designed to punish Boston and Massachusetts.

The Continental Congresses and the Declaration of Independence

In 1774, delegates from all of the colonies except Georgia met in Philadelpnia for the First Continental Congress. They wanted to determine how they should react to the actions of the British government. The delegates agreed to boycott British goods, petition King George III to restore colonial rights, and begin military preparations to resist British policies. In response to the petition, the British declared Massachusetts to be rebellious. Fighting began at Lexington and Concord in April 1775.

The Second Continental Congress met in May 1775. The Congress authorized the formation of an army under the command of George Washington. At the same time it petitioned the king to protect colonial rights. In January 1776, Thomas Paine published a pamphlet called *Common Sense*, urging the colonies to declare independence. Eventually, in July 1776, the Congress issued the Declaration of Independence and committed fully to the Revolutionary War, which lasted until 1783. In that year, Great Britain went down in defeat, and the United States became a new, independent nation.

The Articles of Confederation and the Constitution

In 1777, a constitution for the united colonies was drafted—the Articles of Confederation. This document established a weak central government that could not even raise taxes to pay the nation's expenses. Still, it served the nation until 1787, when a convention to revise it was held. A draft of the new document, the Constitution, was approved after 17 weeks of debate; it took four years for all the states to ratify it. The Bill of Rights, protecting essential rights of citizens, was added after the Constitution was ratified. The Constitution provided for a much stronger central government than had the Articles of Confederation. This stronger government helped ensure the survival of the new nation.

U.S. History Practice 2

Choose the one best answer to each question.

1. According to the passage, why did Great Britain begin to pay more attention to the American colonies in the mid-1700s?

    (1) Before fighting against the French and Indian War, it needed colonial support.
    (2) It needed to protect its North American empire and to tax the colonists to pay for wars.
    (3) The colonies exported tea to Great Britain, which Great Britain needed.
    (4) The colonies were adding substantial economic strength to Great Britain.
    (5) The colonies were beginning to revolt.

2. Which document announced the colonies' break from British rule?

    (1) the Proclamation of 1763
    (2) *Common Sense*
    (3) the Declaration of Independence
    (4) the Articles of Confederation
    (5) the U.S. Constitution

3. Based on the passage, which colonial action succeeded in reversing some British policies?

    (1) helping fight the French and Indian War
    (2) petitioning the king
    (3) boycotting British goods
    (4) moving west of the Appalachians
    (5) meetings of delegates from all colonies

4. Which principle of government was violated by taxing the colonies when the colonies had no representation in Parliament?

    (1) A government can rule only with the consent of the governed.
    (2) Disputes between two parties should be settled by an impartial third party.
    (3) Different branches of government should have different powers.
    (4) All citizens should have the right to express themselves freely.
    (5) The government has no right to censor the press.

5. How did the actions of the Second Continental Congress reveal differing points of view about its policy toward Great Britain?

    (1) It was made up of delegates from all of the colonies.
    (2) It eventually committed the colonies to fight in the Revolutionary War.
    (3) It issued the Declaration of Independence.
    (4) It formed an army to fight Britain and also petitioned the king to restore rights.
    (5) It appointed George Washington to lead the army.

Questions 6 and 7 refer to this circle graph.

Occupations of the Framers of the Constitution

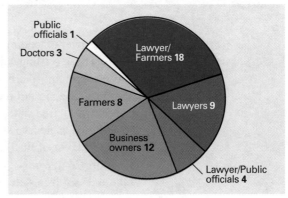

6. How many framers of the Constitution were doctors?

    (1) 18   (4) 3
    (2) 12   (5) 1
    (3) 4

7. Which of the following conclusions is supported by data from the graph?

    (1) More than half of the framers were lawyers.
    (2) Farmers made up the majority of the delegates working on the Constitution.
    (3) Most of the framers were from Virginia.
    (4) Most of the framers were from Georgia.
    (5) More than 100 public officials helped frame the Constitution.

Answers and explanations start on page 87.

Westward Expansion

By 1860, the United States had expanded to the Pacific coast, as shown in the map below. Settlers pushed west, displacing Indian tribes. Canals and railroads were built to provide transport for people and goods through many parts of the nation.

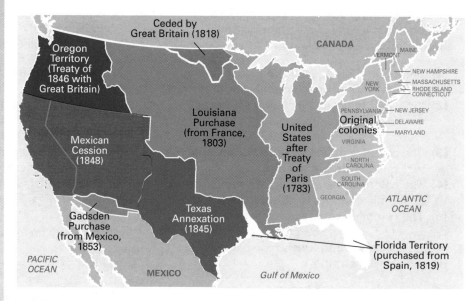

Sectionalism

Disputes over extending slavery into the new territories arose during the early 1800s. Those settling southern territories favored slavery for economic reasons. Those settling northern territories were generally opposed to slavery. When Missouri, a section of the Louisiana Purchase, applied for statehood in 1819, there were 11 free states and 11 slave states. The North did not want Missouri to be admitted as a slave state because that would tip the balance of power in the Senate in favor of the South. After months of debate, Congress reached the Missouri Compromise: (1) Missouri was admitted as a slave state, (2) Maine was admitted as a free state, and (3) slavery was prohibited in the rest of the Louisiana Purchase. Although the Missouri Compromise settled the immediate dispute, it did nothing to relieve the sectionalism, or loyalty to a particular region, that eventually led to the Civil War.

The Civil War

Differences over slavery, disagreement over states' rights and the rights of the federal government, and economic differences between the industrializing North and the agricultural South all caused great tensions in the 1850s. In 1860, Abraham Lincoln, from the Republican Party, which opposed the expansion of slavery, was elected president by the populous northern states. Lincoln's election triggered the secession, or withdrawal, of seven Southern states from the Union. After Lincoln took office in 1861, the Southern rebellion grew into an all-out war, the Civil War. Although the Union won in 1865 and slavery was abolished, the war was extremely costly and destructive of both life and property.

U.S. History Practice 3

Choose the <u>one best answer</u> to each question.

1. Based on the map, which acquisition nearly doubled the area of the United States?

   (1) the Louisiana Purchase, 1803
   (2) the Florida Territory, 1819
   (3) the Texas Annexation, 1845
   (4) the Oregon Territory, 1846
   (5) Mexican Cession, 1848

2. What is the best title for the map?

   (1) The United States
   (2) U.S. Land Acquisitions from Mexico
   (3) The Original Thirteen States
   (4) The United States after the Treaty of Paris
   (5) Westward Expansion of the United States to 1860

3. What was the reason that simply admitting Missouri as a slave state in 1819 would have shifted the balance of power in the Senate?

   (1) Eventually the entire Louisiana Purchase would have entered the Union as slave states.
   (2) Despite the fact that Missouri was a slave state, it would have aligned itself with the industrial North.
   (3) Representation in the Senate was proportional to a state's population.
   (4) Senators usually voted along regional lines, and admitting Missouri would have given the South a majority by two votes.
   (5) Slaves were not permitted to vote in state or federal elections.

4. *Manifest destiny* was the phrase used to describe the U.S. goal of expanding westward across North America. Which of these furthered the goal of manifest destiny?

   (1) Maine's admission as a state in 1820
   (2) the annexation of Texas in 1845
   (3) the secession of South Carolina in 1860
   (4) the freeing of slaves in the Confederacy in 1863
   (5) the end of the Civil War in 1865

5. In 1863, Lincoln issued the Emancipation Proclamation. In it, he declared that all slaves in the rebelling states were free. Even though no slaves were immediately freed, why was the proclamation important?

   (1) It was the first step the U.S. government took to abolish slavery.
   (2) It gave slaves the right to vote.
   (3) It drafted slaves into the U.S. army.
   (4) It made the Southern states end their rebellion.
   (5) Plantations could be better run without slaves.

<u>Question 6</u> refers to the following graph.

Military Casualties of the Civil War

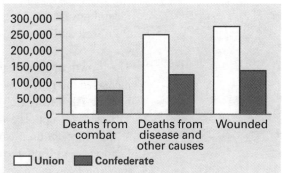

Source: U.S. Civil War Center, Louisiana State University

6. Which of the following statements about the Civil War is confirmed by data in this graph?

   (1) In total, about 250,000 soldiers died.
   (2) In total, about 200,000 soldiers were wounded.
   (3) Compared with the Union army, a higher percentage of soldiers in the Confederate army were killed.
   (4) Civil War soldiers had more to fear from illness, malnutrition, and exposure than from combat.
   (5) In total, there were more casualties in the Civil War than in the Revolutionary War.

Answers and explanations start on page 87.

The Second Industrial Revolution: Oil and Steel

As it did in Great Britain, the American Industrial Revolution began in the textile industry. New England mills began manufacturing yarn and cloth in the 1790s. By the 1860s, production began to shift to heavy industry. The oil and steel industries grew rapidly.

In the 1870s, Andrew Carnegie started manufacturing steel in Pittsburgh using the most advanced technology of the day. He followed a business strategy called vertical integration, in which he controlled all stages of the industrial process, from mining iron ore to shipping the finished steel. By 1900, Carnegie Steel produced more steel than all the steel mills in Great Britain. In the oil refining industry, John D. Rockefeller established a similarly powerful company—Standard Oil. His business strategy was horizontal integration. Rockefeller bought out his competitors until his company, called a trust, had a monopoly.

The Effects of Industrialization

The concentration of industry in powerful trusts caused a backlash. In 1890, Congress passed the Sherman Antitrust Act, which forbade contracts and combinations that would curtail competition and restrain trade. However, the law was too weak to stop the continued growth of trusts. In the early 1900s, the federal government began serious "trust busting" under Presidents Theodore Roosevelt and Woodrow Wilson.

The growth of American industry raised the standard of living, but it also increased the gulf between rich and poor. Men like Carnegie and Rockefeller became fabulously rich, but most Americans worked for wages that were not sufficient to support a family. As a result, in many families both parents as well as the older children worked. Low wages and poor working conditions in factories contributed to labor unrest in the late 1800s. Laborers tried to organize into unions to increase their power, but management fought them. Conflicts between labor and management were often violent, and soldiers were sometimes needed to control outbreaks, as shown in the drawing on page 31.

A Nation of Immigrants

There was a surplus of cheap labor in the late 1800s and early 1900s because millions of immigrants came to the United States. This large migration was partly the result of "push" factors in Europe. For example, increased agricultural productivity led to a surplus of farm workers. In addition, "pull" factors made the United States the destination of choice for many. The large number of jobs for unskilled workers held out the promise of opportunity here. In addition, those seeking religious freedom, like the Jews of Russia and Eastern Europe, also chose the United States. Roman Catholics and Orthodox Christians from southern and eastern Europe and Ireland also came in great numbers. As a result, the population of the United States became more diverse.

U.S. History Practice 4

Choose the <u>one best answer</u> to each question.

1. Which of the following does the passage imply contributed most to the economic success of the steel and oil industries?

   (1) the use of traditional technologies
   (2) the formation of trusts to decrease competition
   (3) good labor-management relations
   (4) a skilled labor force
   (5) cheap natural resources

2. Where were most immigrants entering the United States in the late 1800s originally from?

   (1) southern and eastern Europe
   (2) England, France, and Scandinavia
   (3) China and South Asia
   (4) Central America and the Caribbean
   (5) South America

3. In the late 1800s, Horatio Alger wrote novels in which poor young men became rich and successful through honesty, hard work, and a bit of luck. These rags-to-riches stories contributed to the idea that anyone could succeed in America with enough effort.

   Which of the following Americans provided an example for rags-to-riches stories?

   (1) Thomas O'Donnell, a poor Irish immigrant who worked on and off in Massachusetts textile mills
   (2) Andrew Carnegie, a poor Scottish immigrant who became a steel tycoon in Pennsylvania
   (3) Milton Leeper, who staked a claim on land in Nebraska but was driven off by grasshoppers before he could begin farming
   (4) President Theodore Roosevelt, who was descended from wealthy Dutch landowners in the Hudson River Valley
   (5) Frances Willard, an educated, middle-class woman who became head of the Women's Christian Temperance Union

4. What is the most likely reason that the Sherman Antitrust Act of 1890 was so weak?

   (1) Congress was set on breaking up trusts.
   (2) The trusts lobbied for a weakened bill.
   (3) The power of the trusts was not well understood.
   (4) Trusts could be controlled by state governments.
   (5) It was thought that government should regulate business.

Question 5 refers to this drawing, published in the magazine *Harper's Weekly* in 1894.

The Granger Collection, New York.

5. How did the artist use detail to indicate he had greater sympathy for the soldiers than for the teeming crowd of workers?

   (1) by extending the crane from the foreground to the middle of the picture
   (2) by tilting a railway car near the crane platform to show the railway car had been damaged
   (3) by showing individual faces of the soldiers to humanize them
   (4) by showing puffs of smoke rising from the soldiers' guns to indicate action
   (5) by showing the workers in a tight group flowing among the buildings

Answers and explanations start on page 87.

U.S. Imperialism

During the first hundred years of its existence, the United States concentrated on expanding westward and limiting European influence in the Americas. After the Civil War, foreign policy began to shift, partly as a result of industrialization. The nation needed sources of raw materials and markets for its goods, so isolationism was no longer practical. The period between 1870 and 1914 has been called the Age of Imperialism (see page 22). During this time, the United States became a world power with territories in Central America (the Panama Canal zone), the Caribbean (Cuba), and the Pacific (the Philippines).

The World Wars and the Great Depression

When World War I broke out in Europe in 1914, the United States attempted to remain neutral. However, Germany's use of submarine warfare against passenger ships, which caused American deaths, led to the U.S. entry into the war in 1917 on the side of Great Britain and the Allied Powers. After the war, President Woodrow Wilson was instrumental in the formation of the League of Nations, the first international peacekeeping organization.

The 1920s were an economic boom time that ended with the collapse of the stock market in 1929. This led to the Great Depression, the worst economic decline in modern history. By 1932, 25 percent of Americans were unemployed. Despite President Franklin Roosevelt's attempts to jump-start the economy with New Deal programs, complete recovery came only when the nation started mobilizing for World War II in the early 1940s.

Social Movements

After World War II, there was great social change in the United States. Women moved into the workforce in great numbers during the 1960s and 1970s. African Americans campaigned for equal rights, using demonstrations, civil disobedience, and the courts to enforce their civil rights. The civil rights movement contributed to activism in other areas, including environmental protection.

The Cold War and Its Aftermath

During this period, the United States became a military superpower and a very important leader in world affairs. The postwar years were tense, with an ever-present threat of conflict with the communist Soviet Union. This conflict, called the Cold War, dominated U.S. foreign policy for over four decades, beginning in the late 1940s. The U.S. goal was initially to contain communism to the nations that had fallen under Soviet influence as the result of World War II. The containment policy led to wars in Korea and Vietnam and crises elsewhere. After 1991, when the Soviet Union collapsed, the United States emerged as the world's most powerful nation. The threat of communism receded and other threats, mainly the spread of nuclear weapons and rise of Islamic fundamentalism, came to the fore with the attacks on the World Trade Center and the Pentagon in September 2001.

U.S. History Practice 5

Choose the <u>one best answer</u> to each question.

1. Based on the passage, why did the United States enter World War I?

   (1) U.S. policy was to maintain a high level of involvement in European politics.
   (2) The League of Nations had failed to prevent war.
   (3) The United States needed to protect its imperial interests in the Pacific.
   (4) Great Britain was blockading Germany.
   (5) Germany torpedoed ocean liners, killing several hundred U.S. passengers.

2. To what present-day organization is the League of Nations most similar?

   (1) the United Nations, an international peacekeeping organization
   (2) the Central Intelligence Agency, a U.S. government department that gathers intelligence abroad
   (3) the Organization of American States, a group of Western Hemisphere nations
   (4) the International Red Cross, which offers disaster relief and other aid
   (5) the World Health Organization, which monitors global health issues

3. Which is the best indicator of the severity of the Great Depression?

   (1) the 1929 stock market crash
   (2) the previous decade of economic boom
   (3) the New Deal programs
   (4) the extremely high unemployment rate
   (5) the mobilization for World War II

4. What was a major difference between the United States and the Soviet Union that led to the Cold War?

   (1) disagreement about the wartime alliance
   (2) disputes over exchanging prisoners of war
   (3) disagreement about the role of the United Nations
   (4) conflict over civil rights for minorities
   (5) commitment to different economic and political systems

5. Based on the passage, how is the U.S. role in today's world best described?

   (1) promoter of isolationism
   (2) leader of the League of Nations
   (3) container of communist imperialism
   (4) the sole superpower
   (5) a fortress of neutrality

<u>Question 6</u> refers to the following information and map.

In 1990, Saddam Hussein of Iraq invaded Kuwait to gain control of its oil. In the 1991 Gulf War, the United States and a coalition of 27 other nations succeeded in driving Iraqi troops out of Kuwait. Saddam Hussein remained in power in Iraq.

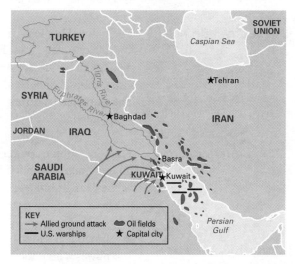

6. What evidence from the map indicates that the goal of the coalition was to liberate Kuwait but not to conquer Iraq?

   (1) Ground forces massed in Saudi Arabia.
   (2) Coalition forces fought close to Basra.
   (3) Coalition forces went only as far as the Euphrates River.
   (4) U.S. warships were in the Persian Gulf.
   (5) Iranian oil fields on the border with Iraq were left untouched.

Answers and explanations start on page 87.

The U.S. Constitution divides the functions of government among three separate branches: the legislative, executive, and judicial branches.

The Legislative Branch

The legislative branch—the U.S. Congress—makes all federal laws. It has two parts: the Senate and the House of Representatives. Voters in each state elect two senators and a number of representatives in proportion to the state's population. Congress has several major powers: (1) the power to tax and spend, which enables it to control both economic and non-economic policies; (2) the power to declare war and regulate commerce with foreign nations; (3) the power to regulate commerce among the states; and (4) the power to remove federal officials, including the president, from office via impeachment.

The Executive Branch

The executive branch enforces the laws of the federal government. It consists of the president, who is elected for a maximum of two four-year terms, and the federal bureaucracy. The president submits legislation to Congress, nominates federal judges, commands the armed forces, and makes foreign policy and treaties. A president's power depends to a great extent on the individual in office and how he or she chooses to use the office to shape U.S. public policy.

The Judicial Branch

The judicial branch, which consists of the Supreme Court and other federal courts, interprets laws. Federal judges are appointed by the president and confirmed by the Senate. Federal courts hear cases in which federal law is at issue, foreign nations are involved, or questions of constitutionality have arisen. The Supreme Court can declare laws passed by Congress or regulations formulated by the executive branch unconstitutional.

Separation of Powers

The separation of powers among the three branches of government ensures that no one branch or individual can become too powerful. The power of each branch is checked, or limited, by the powers of the other branches, resulting in a system of checks and balance among government branches.

- In the legislative branch, both houses of Congress must pass a law, checking power within the legislature. In addition, the president can veto laws passed by Congress, and the Supreme Court can rule laws unconstitutional.
- The executive branch is checked by Congress when it rejects laws the president wants passed, overrides a presidential veto, or votes to impeach the president or other officials. The Supreme Court can declare acts of the president unconstitutional.
- The judicial branch is checked by Congress through its power to change the jurisdiction of the courts, block appointment of federal judges, impeach federal judges, and amend the Constitution.

Civics and Government Practice 1

Choose the <u>one best answer</u> to each question.

1. According to the passage, which of these is a major power of the legislative branch?

   (1) declaring laws unconstitutional
   (2) making treaties with foreign nations
   (3) nominating federal judges
   (4) running the federal bureaucracy
   (5) controlling the federal budget

2. Most federal judges, including Supreme Court justices, are appointed for life terms. What is the most likely reason that these judges have life terms?

   (1) Appointing judges for short terms would create too much work for the president.
   (2) Appointing judges for short terms would take too much time in Congress.
   (3) Having job security protects judges from political pressure when making rulings.
   (4) Most judges are middle-aged or old when they are appointed.
   (5) Each political party wants to appoint its own judges.

3. The president sends representatives to an international conference to negotiate an agreement on trade. Which power is the president exercising?

   (1) the right to appoint federal judges
   (2) the right to make treaties with other nations
   (3) the ability to propose legislation
   (4) the right to veto legislation
   (5) the role of commander-in-chief

4. What aspect of human nature were the framers of the U.S. Constitution trying to control through the distribution of functions among three branches of government?

   (1) the abuse of power
   (2) the ability to reason
   (3) the exercise of fairness
   (4) the preference for order over chaos
   (5) the need for freedom

Questions 5 and 6 refer to the diagram below.

How a Bill Becomes a Law

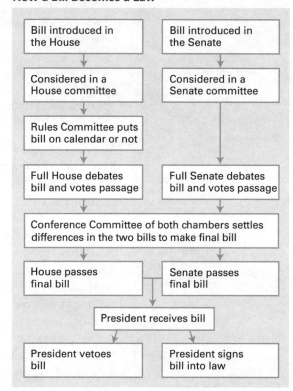

5. What does the diagram imply about the process by which a bill becomes a law?

   (1) All bills are introduced in the House.
   (2) Debate takes place only in the Senate.
   (3) The Rules Committee decides which bills go to the full House.
   (4) Senate committees work very quickly.
   (5) Both House and Senate versions of a bill go to the president.

6. A bill can be rejected at any stage of the process. Which conclusion is supported by this fact and the information in the diagram?

   (1) Legislators agree on all bills introduced.
   (2) Introducing a bill ensures its rejection.
   (3) Most bills are killed during debate.
   (4) The president often vetoes bills.
   (5) Most bills never become law.

Answers and explanations start on page 88.

Federalism

The U.S. Constitution established a federal system of government in which power is divided between the national government and the governments of the states.

Powers of the National (Federal) Government	Powers of the State Governments
Declare war, raise armies	Maintain state militias
Regulate interstate commerce, imports, and exports	Regulate commerce within the state
Regulate immigration and naturalization	
Set taxes	Set taxes
Borrow money	Borrow money
Coin money	
Make laws to help it carry out its assigned powers	Exercise powers not specifically granted to the federal government

All powers that are not reserved for the national government belong to the states. As a result, our federal system allows for great regional diversity. However, in Article VI, the Constitution states that when there is a direct conflict between national and state law, national law "shall be the supreme Law of the Land."

Amending the Constitution

In Article V, the Constitution outlines the process required to amend, or change, the document. Amendments can be proposed by a two-thirds vote in both the House and Senate. They can also be proposed by a national convention called at the request of two-thirds of the state legislatures. To be added to the Constitution, the amendment must then be ratified by the legislatures or special conventions of three-quarters of the states. The Constitution has been amended 27 times.

The Bill of Rights

When the Constitution was first drafted in 1787, many states opposed it because it did not explicitly guarantee the rights and liberties of citizens. Several states ratified the Constitution only after legislators agreed to spell out these rights in a set of amendments to the Constitution. This set of amendments is called the Bill of Rights. The Bill of Rights was adopted in 1791 and includes:

* The First Amendment, guaranteeing freedom of speech, the press, religion, and assembly
* The Second Amendment, guaranteeing the right of citizens to bear arms
* The Third Amendment, preventing the quartering of troops in private homes, unless stipulated by law during a war
* The Fourth Amendment, protecting against unreasonable search and seizure
* The Fifth Amendment, outlining the rights of people accused of crimes
* The Sixth Amendment, providing for speedy and public criminal trials by jury
* The Seventh Amendment, providing for jury trials in civil cases
* The Eighth Amendment, providing freedom from cruel and unusual punishment, excessive fines, or excessive bail

Civics and Government Practice 2

Choose the <u>one best answer</u> to each question.

1. Which of the following is a power belonging to the states alone?

   (1) to declare war
   (2) to regulate immigration
   (3) to regulate in-state commerce
   (4) to levy taxes
   (5) to coin money

2. What is the purpose of the Bill of Rights?

   (1) to protect the rights of ordinary citizens
   (2) to protect the rights of the states
   (3) to allocate power between the states and the federal government
   (4) to provide a process by which the Constitution can be amended
   (5) to divide power among the branches of government

3. Most nations do not have a federal form of government. Instead, they centralize power in a national government, and local governments just have an administrative role. What is the most likely reason the framers of the Constitution chose a federal system in which power is divided between levels of government?

   (1) to make government more efficient
   (2) to standardize laws in the nation
   (3) to concentrate power in the national government
   (4) to place a check on the power of the national government
   (5) to weaken the state governments

4. Which of the following is an example of a federal power?

   (1) raising local property taxes
   (2) changing the rates for state income taxes
   (3) setting standards for local highway construction
   (4) establishing a process for becoming a citizen
   (5) preventing newspapers from publishing editorials critical of its policies

5. An argument opposing gun control laws can be made by citing which amendment?

   (1) the First Amendment
   (2) the Second Amendment
   (3) the Fourth Amendment
   (4) the Sixth Amendment
   (5) the Eighth Amendment

<u>Questions 6 and 7</u> refer to the following map.

Executions by State, 2004

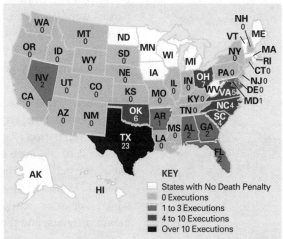

6. Which state had the most executions in 2004?

   (1) North Carolina
   (2) Ohio
   (3) Oklahoma
   (4) Texas
   (5) Virginia

7. Which question can be answered by looking at the map?

   (1) When was the last execution in Maine?
   (2) How many convicted criminals are awaiting execution?
   (3) How many executions took place in the year 2000?
   (4) How many states require the death penalty for those who kill police officers?
   (5) Does federal law require the death penalty for violent crimes?

Answers and explanations start on page 88.

Political Parties

A political party is a group of citizens, party officials, and elected office-holders who have a common identity. Parties are a link between the ordinary voter and government, as well as a link between officials in different levels and branches of government. The goal of a political party is to influence public policy by electing its members to public office. A party may have an ideology and a stated position on issues, but in practice its members may depart from the party line in order to get elected and stay in office.

There are two main parties in the United States, the Democrats and the Republicans. Most voters identify themselves with one of the major parties, although the number of independent voters has increased substantially in the last few decades.

Occasionally a third party arises. The most recent third parties were Ross Perot's Reform Party and Ralph Nader's Green Party. Third parties do not usually last long. The most significant aspect of third parties in recent years is that they can affect elections by attracting votes that would normally go to one of the two major parties.

Interest Groups

Another way that citizens influence government is through membership in special interest groups. Special interest groups form around relatively narrow interests, such as occupation (American Institute of CPAs), age (American Association of Retired Persons), race or ethnicity (League of United Latin American Citizens), environmental concerns (Audubon Society), or political concerns (Mothers Against Drunk Driving). Members pay dues to support the group's activities, which consist primarily of lobbying—efforts to influence political candidates, public officials, and the direction of public policy.

Election Campaigns

Candidates for political office conduct political campaigns to get elected. There are two main stages to a political campaign. The first is the nomination campaign, in which each party chooses candidates through primaries or conventions. Once a candidate is nominated by her party, she enters the second stage—the general election campaign. At this point she tries to persuade the majority of voters, of any party, to vote for her. Campaigns are conducted by personal appearances, volunteers who raise money and contact voters, and the media. A media campaign consists both of "free" exposure, such as news articles or TV news broadcasts, and paid political advertising.

In the presidential campaign in 2004, the Internet played a large role for the first time. Candidates and political organizations raised money, issued news releases, and sent out e-mail to supporters from their web sites. The Internet made direct participation by millions of voters in the campaign relatively easy.

Civics and Government Practice 3

Choose the <u>one best answer</u> to each question.

1. According to the passage, what is the main goal of a political party?

   (1) to enact specific legislation
   (2) to get its candidates elected
   (3) to represent under-represented voters
   (4) to represent regional interests
   (5) to lobby for its interests

2. By which of the following methods do special interest groups most often pursue the interests of their members?

   (1) by voting
   (2) by lobbying
   (3) by running candidates for office
   (4) by forming political parties
   (5) by running election campaigns

3. In Maryville, the city council is up for election, but the mayor is not. All residents receive a brochure that says: Support Mayor Doyle. Vote Republican on Election Day!

   Who most likely sent this brochure?

   (1) the city council
   (2) the local Democratic Party
   (3) the local Republican Party
   (4) a citizens' reform group
   (5) the mayor's campaign

4. During campaigns, politicians can be very vague on certain issues to prevent alienating voters. What attitude does this reflect?

   (1) a strong moral clarity on issues
   (2) a need to stake out a position
   (3) an emphasis on party loyalty
   (4) a commitment to basic values
   (5) a practical approach to getting elected

5. What is a third party?

   (1) a branch of the Democratic party
   (2) a branch of the Republican party
   (3) any party other than the Democrats or Republicans
   (4) the third U.S. political party ever formed
   (5) an important lobbying group

6. What do political parties and special interest groups have in common?

   (1) They both run candidates for office.
   (2) They both appeal to narrow interests.
   (3) They both serve as ways to link the citizen with the government.
   (4) They both conduct political election campaigns.
   (5) The United States has only two of each.

Question 7 refers to the following graph.

Political Party Affiliation of Governors, 1975–2004

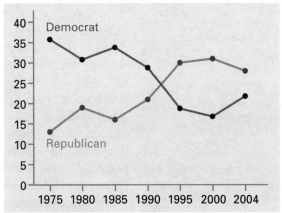

Source: National Governors Association

7. Which of the following best summarizes the information shown in this graph?

   (1) From 1975 to 2004, the number of Democratic and Republican governors fell.
   (2) From 1975 to 2004, the number of Democratic and Republican governors rose.
   (3) From 1975 to 2004, the number of Democratic governors rose and the number of Republican governors fell.
   (4) From 1975 to 2004, the number of Democratic governors fell and the number of Republican governors rose.
   (5) In 2004, there were more Democratic than Republican governors.

Answers and explanations start on page 88.

Liberties and Rights

The Bill of Rights, ratified in 1791, protects many civil liberties: freedom of speech, assembly, religion, the press, and so on (see page 36). Over time, amendments to the Constitution have explicitly added more civil rights.

- The Thirteenth Amendment abolished slavery (1865).
- The Fourteenth Amendment extended the guarantee of citizens' rights to their dealings with the states as well as with the federal government. It says that the states cannot "deprive any person of life, liberty, or property, without due process of law" (1868).
- The Fifteenth Amendment gave voting rights to all adult men (1870).
- The Nineteenth Amendment gave women the right to vote (1920).
- The Twenty-Sixth Amendment gave the vote to all citizens 18 years old or older (1971).

Voting and Other Forms of Participation in the Democratic Process

There are many ways for citizens to participate in a representative democracy. The most basic of these is to vote for the people who will represent them at the local, state, and federal levels of government. In 1964, in *Westburry* v. *Sanders*, the Supreme Court ruled that the right to vote is the basis of all other political rights. Although the right to vote is granted to citizens 18 or older, the states can restrict the voting rolls to a certain extent. For example, most states do not permit insane people, convicted felons, or resident aliens to vote.

Individuals can also participate in politics and the community in other ways. Some volunteer to work on political campaigns, and some contribute money to political candidates. Others contact public officials by mail, phone, or e-mail to express their opinions on issues and to influence the official's actions. Still others join interest groups and help with lobbying, protests, demonstrations, and civil disobedience.

Some Duties of Citizenship

Serving on a jury is one of the duties of citizenship. Any criminal defendant who faces a sentence of six months or more is eligible to be tried by a jury of his peers—ordinary citizens—who will decide whether or not he is guilty as charged. In addition, civil trials also need jurors to decide the merits of the case. Juries serve to protect the accused from the possible tyranny of particular government prosecutors or judges. Either consensus or a majority vote is needed to make a jury decision.

Another duty of citizens is military service. During most of U.S. history, the nation has had an all-volunteer military, and the states have had all-volunteer National Guard units. At times, Congress has instituted a draft to conscript soldiers to meet the needs of the armed forces. During the Vietnam War, for example, the draft was based on a lottery system. Men who received a low number were drafted; those with a high number did not have to serve. Serving in the military unites Americans from widely varying backgrounds and helps reinforce the values upon which the nation was founded.

Civics and Government Practice 4

Choose the <u>one best answer</u> to each question.

1. According to the Supreme Court decision in *Westburry* v. *Sanders*, which is the most basic political right?

   (1) the right to life
   (2) freedom of speech
   (3) the right ⁺o privacy
   (4) freedom of the press
   (5) the right to vote

2. Which of the following people would be denied the right to vote by most states?

   (1) a resident alien
   (2) a holder of political office
   (3) a naturalized citizen
   (4) a citizen over age 70
   (5) a citizen who did not complete elementary school

3. When she turned 18, Ramona registered to vote. Which constitutional amendments gave Ramona the right to do this?

   (1) the Thirteenth and Fourteenth
   (2) the Fourteenth and Fifteenth
   (3) the Fifteenth and Nineteenth
   (4) the Nineteenth and Twenty-Sixth
   (5) the Twenty-Sixth and Thirteenth

4. When the nation is involved in a war that is unpopular or that lasts for a prolonged period, lawmakers consider instituting a draft. Which of the following could be used to support a proposal for drafting soldiers?

   (1) Recruitment and reenlistment figures drop during protracted warfare.
   (2) Modern warfare is very technical and requires more training than can be given draftees.
   (3) On average, draftees are less well educated than volunteers.
   (4) An all-volunteer army has soldiers who are highly motivated to succeed.
   (5) An all-volunteer army is more professional than an army of draftees.

5. Which value underlies the series of amendments extending voting rights?

   (1) the right to life
   (2) the right to liberty
   (3) freedom of assembly
   (4) equal rights for all
   (5) the lawfulness of contracts

<u>Questions 6 and 7</u> refer to the following editorial cartoon.

Gary Markstein/Milwaukee Journal.

6. Who does the man on the right represent?

   (1) a candidate for political office
   (2) a potential juror
   (3) a nonvoter
   (4) a campaign volunteer
   (5) a pollster

7. According to the cartoonist, what causes low turnout in this country's elections?

   (1) barriers to voter registration
   (2) citizens' lack of knowledge about and interest in politics
   (3) the frequency of presidential elections
   (4) the need to take time off work to vote
   (5) the fact that many voters are polled before election day

Answers and explanations start on page 88.

Economics is the study of how resources are used to satisfy people's needs and wants. Since resources are scarce compared to needs and wants, people must make choices about how resources are used.

A Market Economy

Every society has an economic system to organize the way economic choices are made. In a market economy, or free enterprise system, economic choices are left largely to the actions of individuals and businesses. People base their choices on prices in the market. A market is a network of dealings between buyers and sellers. Buying and selling may take place in a particular location or at a distance, by mail, phone, fax, or Internet.

For example, consider the market for flat panel TVs. Manufacturers compete with one another to produce flat panel TVs that they think consumers will want to buy. A consumer shopping for a flat panel TV will choose a model that combines good features with a competitive price. When conditions in the market change, the behavior of consumers and producers changes as well. For instance, a scarcity of highly desirable Brand X flat panel TVs will lead to a price increase. Because of the higher price, consumers may decide to buy less desirable, but cheaper Brands Y and Z. At the Brand X factory, managers will try to increase production to meet the demand. They may even lower the price, as well.

The Profit Motive and Private Property

In a market economy, people are motivated to produce goods and services because they may make a profit. A profit is money left over for the producer of a good or service after he or she has paid all expenses necessary to produce the good or service. In a market economy, the profit motive is supported by a legal system that protects private ownership of property. The assurance that your profits will remain yours (aside from taxes) encourages free enterprise and innovation.

Other Economic Systems

There are other types of economic systems. In a centrally directed economy, or command economy, most production is controlled by the government. Government agencies decide what to produce, how much to produce, and for whom to produce goods and services. If supplies of a product run low, the government may limit the amount a customer may buy. The former Soviet Union and its satellite nations had centrally directed economies whose inefficiency helped lead to the collapse of these nations. Today most are shifting toward a market economy.

Another type of economy is the traditional economy, typical of nonindustrialized nations trying to modernize. In these economies, custom dictates the way economic decisions are made. Some of the agricultural economies of Africa are examples of traditional economies.

Most nations, including the United States, have mixed economies. The United States has a market economy with government regulation and some government ownership, for example of highways, dams, and land.

Economics Practice 1

Choose the <u>one best answer</u> to each question.

1. According to the passage, what is a market?

   (1) a web of transactions between buyers and sellers
   (2) a place where things are on display
   (3) the allocation of resources
   (4) the relationship between individuals and companies
   (5) the government agency that makes economic decisions

2. Why do people take risks and work hard to produce things in a market economy?

   (1) to sell their labor
   (2) to adjust prices freely
   (3) to make a profit
   (4) to use up their resources
   (5) to benefit society as a whole

3. What is the most likely result of an oversupply of DVD players on the market?

   (1) Customers will stop buying DVD players.
   (2) The price of DVD players will fall.
   (3) DVD manufacturers will increase production.
   (4) DVD players will be replaced by the next technology.
   (5) DVD manufacturers will make greater profits.

4. What value underlies the workings of a centrally directed economy?

   (1) the drive for success
   (2) a tolerance of uncertainty
   (3) a respect for individual differences
   (4) equal opportunity for all
   (5) a need for order and control

5. How is the U.S. economy classified?

   (1) as a profit economy
   (2) as a scarcity economy
   (3) as a command economy
   (4) as a traditional economy
   (5) as a mixed economy

6. Goods are physical products for sale. Services consist of work done for others. Which of the following would be classified as goods?

   (1) dry cleaning   **(4)** clothing
   (2) computer repair   **(5)** housekeeping
   (3) daycare

Questions 7 and 8 refer to the following information and graph.

The demand for a product is the amount that consumers would like to buy at a particular price. The supply of a product is the amount suppliers would like to sell at a particular price. The graph shows the supply and demand for potato chips.

Supply and Demand for Potato Chips

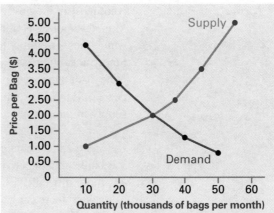

7. If the price for a bag of potato chips is $3.00, about how many bags are consumers likely to buy?

   (1) 10,000   **(3)** 30,000   **(5)** 50,000
   (2) 20,000   **(4)** 40,000

8. The equilibrium price is the price at which the amount that buyers are willing to buy equals the amount that sellers are willing to sell. What is the equilibrium price per bag for potato chips in this market?

   (1) $1.00   **(3)** $2.50   **(5)** $3.50
   (2) $2.00   **(4)** $3.00

Answers and explanations start on page 88.

The Government as Producer and Consumer

The government plays a large role in the U.S. economy. First, the government produces public goods. These are goods and services that it is not practical for individuals or businesses to produce. Examples include the armed services and the interstate highway system. Second, the government buys goods and services from the  private sector, such as paper, computers, fighter jets, and management expertise. The federal government is the number one consumer in the nation.

The Federal Budget and Fiscal Policy

Because the federal budget is so large, the government can use its clout to influence the economy. Economies generally have business cycles—boom periods of expansion followed by slowdowns called recessions. The government seeks to smooth out this cycle and minimize the disruption caused by high unemployment or rapidly rising prices. The president and Congress do this through fiscal policy—adjustments in the amounts the government taxes and spends. For example, suppose the economy is slow and businesses are not hiring. Congress can pass laws to increase its own spending in order to create more demand for products, so that businesses will increase their payrolls. As a result, the economy will pick up and the unemployment rate will fall.

Monetary Policy

Another way the government influences the economy is through monetary policy. Monetary policy is under the control of the Federal Reserve Board (the Fed), which meets monthly to manage the nation's money supply and interest rates. Since most businesses depend on loans to operate, they are affected by Fed policy. An increased money supply leads to economic expansion, while a decreased money supply slows economic growth. The Fed influences the money supply in three ways:

1. The Fed can change banks' reserve requirement—the percentage of deposits banks must keep on hand. Raising the reserve requirement makes lending more difficult, decreasing the money supply. Lowering it makes lending easier, increasing the money supply.
2. The Fed can adjust the discount rate, the interest charged to member banks to borrow from the Federal Reserve Bank. Raising the discount rate discourages borrowing and decreases the money supply; lowering it makes borrowing easier and increases the money supply. The discount rate affects consumers, too, because the interest charged on mortgages and other loans depends on the discount rate.
3. The Fed can buy and sell government securities. Buying securities increases the money supply, and selling them decreases it.

Government Regulation

The government also plays a large role in regulating economic activity. It pursues an antitrust policy, breaking up monopolies to encourage competition. It sets safety and pollution standards for certain products and industries. And it protects workers by setting safety standards, granting them the right to form unions, and protecting them against discrimination.

Economics Practice 2

Choose the <u>one best answer</u> to each question.

1. Why do governments produce public goods and services such as firefighting services?

(1) Governments make a profit from public goods and services.
(2) Public goods and services use up government resources.
(3) It is not practical for individuals or companies to produce or obtain them.
(4) The government can't find buyers for these goods and services.
(5) Public goods and services are too complex for the private sector to produce.

2. According to the passage, what is a business cycle?

(1) the taxes paid in two consecutive fiscal years
(2) alternating periods of economic expansion and contraction
(3) the back-and-forth transactions of supplier and consumer
(4) the return of used products for recycling and reuse
(5) the reaction of the economy to federal actions

3. Which of the following actions could the Fed take to stimulate the economy?

(1) lowering the discount rate
(2) raising the reserve requirement
(3) selling government securities
(4) substantially raising taxes
(5) substantially cutting its spending

4. Which of the following is an example of a government agency whose mission is primarily to protect workers?

(1) Occupational Safety and Health Administration
(2) Food and Drug Administration
(3) Consumer Protection Agency
(4) Environmental Protection Agency
(5) Internal Revenue Service

5. Which conclusion about economic policy is supported by information in the passage?

(1) The president controls both fiscal and monetary policy.
(2) Fiscal and monetary policies work only during periods of expansion.
(3) With good fiscal and monetary policies, recessions can be entirely eliminated.
(4) Fiscal policy takes longer to put into action than monetary policy.
(5) It is easy for governments to fine-tune their economies.

Question 6 refers to the following graph.

Federal Expenditures, 2003 (in billions of dollars)

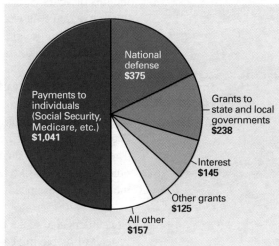

National defense $375

Grants to state and local governments $238

Payments to individuals (Social Security, Medicare, etc.) $1,041

Interest $145

Other grants $125

All other $157

Source: U.S. Office of Management and Budget

6. What portion of the federal budget goes to Social Security, Medicare, and other payments for individuals?

(1) about one-fifth
(2) about one-quarter
(3) about one-third
(4) about one-half
(5) about three-quarters

Answers and explanations start on page 89.

Labor and Wages

Most people participate in the economy by selling their labor as workers and using their earnings, or wages, to buy goods and services as consumers. Like other prices, wages mainly depend on supply and demand. The demand for labor depends on the demand for goods and services by consumers. For example, if consumers want restaurant meals and take-out food, the demand for food service workers will increase. The supply of different types of labor varies greatly and depends on the industry, population figures, education, and training. For some types of jobs, the labor supply has become global. For example, the textile industry has moved from industrialized nations such as the United States to developing nations such as Mexico and China, in order to take advantage of a large supply of cheap labor there. Another example is in agriculture, where the jobs do not move overseas, but the workers move where the jobs are. In the United States, many seasonal agricultural workers are immigrants from Latin America.

Labor Unions

In some industries, workers band together in labor unions to increase their power to negotiate wages, benefits, and working conditions. Through collective bargaining, representatives of the union and management agree on pay and working conditions. Then they sign a contract that lasts for a set period of months or years. When labor and management cannot agree on a contract, the union may have its workers work to rule. This means they follow work procedures and policies to the letter and do not do any extra work. Or, the union can go out on strike.

Consumer Spending and Debt

Workers are also consumers of goods and services. Since most consumers do not have enough money to buy everything they want, they must make choices about what to buy. Spending decisions depend on personal preferences and prices. People generally buy necessities such as shelter, food, clothing, and utilities first. Then, with leftover income, they buy luxuries—items they would like to have but don't really need, like DVD players or vacations. Or they may save the extra money for future needs.

Consumers also make purchases by borrowing money instead of by paying cash. When they do this, they are using consumer credit. For example, consumers take out mortgage loans to buy homes and auto loans to buy cars. But most purchasing on credit takes place with credit cards. By charging a purchase to a credit card, a consumer can have the use of the item immediately, paying for it later. Credit cards bill consumers once a month. If the  consumer pays the entire balance on time, there generally is no charge, or interest, for the use of this money. However, most consumers do not pay off their entire monthly balance. They are charged interest, often at relatively high rates, for the balance remaining on the card. Many U.S. consumers carry large amounts of debt and must pay substantial interest on this debt.

Economics Practice 3

Choose the <u>one best answer</u> to each question.

1. According to the passage, what are wages?

   (1) the cost of necessities
   (2) money invested in business
   (3) the price paid for labor
   (4) dues paid by union members
   (5) the balance carried on a credit card

2. What is consumer credit?

   (1) points consumers earn for buying certain products
   (2) money loaned to consumers to purchase items
   (3) the interest charged on credit cards
   (4) the items consumers buy with income left after necessities have been bought
   (5) the cost associated with working at a job

3. If a large portion of the workforce in an area is unemployed, what is likely to happen to consumer demand in that area?

   (1) Consumer demand for necessities will rise.
   (2) Consumer demand for luxuries will rise.
   (3) Consumer demand will remain steady.
   (4) Consumer demand for goods and services will fall.
   (5) Consumer demand will shift to other nearby places.

4. In addition to labor, land is a resource used to produce goods and services. Land includes all natural resources. Which of the following is an example of land?

   (1) iron ore
   (2) the smelting process
   (3) machine tools
   (4) factories
   (5) steel workers

5. What have textile factory owners gained by moving their factories to Mexico?

   (1) cheap labor
   (2) cheap materials
   (3) cheap land
   (4) high wages
   (5) low demand

6. For representatives of labor and management to successfully negotiate a contract, what must they value most?

   (1) financial benefits for the union
   (2) financial benefits for management
   (3) victory over an opponent
   (4) the power to go out on strike
   (5) the give and take of compromise

<u>Question 7</u> refers to the following ad.

7. What is the main purpose of this ad?

   (1) to remind consumers that Valentine's Day is coming soon
   (2) to persuade consumers to buy the more expensive, larger gift bags
   (3) to demonstrate the superior quality of Deep Discount Stores' gift bags
   (4) to persuade consumers to buy gift bags at Deep Discount Stores
   (5) to compare gift bag brands offered at Deep Discount Stores and ABC Stores

Answers and explanations start on page 89.

Geographers divide the world into regions according to climate, biomes, politics, culture, and other factors.

Climate Zones

The climate of a region is determined primarily by temperature and rainfall. It is also affected by the distribution of land and ocean. Places near the ocean have more moderate climates than regions inland. In addition, mountainous regions have climates different from nearby lowlands. Earth can be divided into climate zones as shown on this map.

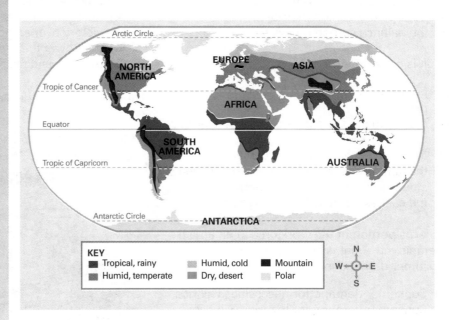

KEY
- ■ Tropical, rainy
- ■ Humid, temperate
- ■ Humid, cold
- ■ Dry, desert
- ■ Mountain
- ■ Polar

Biomes

Climate affects the distribution of plants and animals into biomes, or large ecosystems. Biomes include:

- rain forests, usually found in tropical, rainy climates but also in temperate zones
- savannahs—semi-arid (dry) open tropical grasslands with sparse trees and shrubs
- steppes—temperate grasslands
- deserts—dry areas with little rainfall and sparse plant life
- woodlands—forests generally found in temperate climates
- wetlands—permanently wet land areas such as marshes and swamps
- taiga—areas of pine forest in cold climates
- tundra—regions just south of the Arctic with no trees, low vegetation, and permafrost

Political and Cultural Regions

There are many ways to divide the Earth into regions besides climate and biomes. For example, a division of the world into political regions could follow national boundaries. It could also reflect political alliances or types of governments. Similarly, the world can be divided into cultural regions based on the language, religion, ethnicity, or other characteristics of people living there.

Geography Practice 1

Choose the <u>one best answer</u> to each question.

1. Which is the best title for the map on page 48?

   (1) The World
   (2) Regions of the World
   (3) World Climate Zones
   (4) World Biomes
   (5) World Political Regions

2. Which question can be answered by looking at the map on page 48?

   (1) What is the weather today in Southeast Asia?
   (2) Why are tropical climates located near the Equator?
   (3) What is the average temperature in North America?
   (4) What type of climate does North Africa have?
   (5) In what climate zone do most people live?

3. Which major factors determine the characteristic of a particular biome?

   (1) climate and vegetation only
   (2) vegetation and animal life only
   (3) climate, vegetation, and animal life
   (4) human populations
   (5) political boundaries

4. The northernmost region of Russia is treeless. Only grasses and mosses grow there, and the soil is frozen all year round. Which biome is this?

   (1) savannah
   (2) steppe
   (3) wetland
   (4) taiga
   (5) tundra

5. Some of the best cattle-grazing land in the world is in South America—in Uruguay and central Argentina. Which biome is this?

   (1) steppe
   (2) wetland
   (3) woodland
   (4) taiga
   (5) tundra

6. In some African savannahs, long periods of drought and overgrazing have destroyed vegetation. If these conditions continue, which biome will eventually result?

   (1) steppe   (4) tundra
   (2) desert   (5) taiga
   (3) woodland

<u>Questions 7 and 8</u> refer to this chart on economic activities of some nations in the region of Central Asia.

Nation	Main economic activities
Kazakstan	Mining, steel, farm machinery, grains and cotton, oil and natural gas
Kyrgyzstan	Cotton, tobacco, fruit and grains, tanning, textiles
Tajikistan	Cotton, textiles
Turkmenistan	Natural gas, cotton, and sheep
Uzbekistan	Cotton, gold, and natural gas

7. Which of the following is produced by all of the nations in this region?

   (1) cotton   (4) textiles
   (2) grains   (5) natural gas
   (3) steel

8. Nations do better economically if they have a broad range of resources and industries. Given this fact, which nation in the region is most likely to have economic difficulties?

   (1) Kazakstan because it produces farm machinery
   (2) Kyrgyzstan because it relies on cotton and textiles as well as farming
   (3) Tajikistan because it relies solely on cotton and textiles
   (4) Turkmenistan because it produces natural gas
   (5) Uzbekistan because it doesn't produce steel

Answers and explanations start on page 89.

Characteristics of Culture

Culture consists of patterns of behavior that are characteristic of a group. To a member of a culture, the patterns of behavior are taken for granted and considered the norm. However, when people of different cultures meet, it becomes apparent that cultural patterns can differ widely.

All cultures have categories of traits that are universal. For example, all cultures have language, religion, settlement patterns, foods, arts, sports, and so on. In each culture these general categories take on specific characteristics. For example, in the United States, popular sports include baseball, football, and basketball. In England and Australia, the major sports include cricket, soccer, and rugby. In Canada, hockey is a very popular sport.

Cultural Diffusion

Cultural diffusion refers to the continuous changing and spreading of cultural traits and whole cultures. The Japanese adoption of baseball is an example of cultural diffusion. The American adoption of Japanese martial arts such as judo and karate and the popularity of sushi are other examples. Cultural diffusion takes place in three general ways:

1. **Migration** When people move, they take their cultures with them. People of the same culture tend to migrate and settle together in groups. For example, most major American cities have ethnic neighborhoods, like Chinatown and Little Italy, where immigrant groups have settled. These groups transform their neighborhoods into cultural approximations of their homelands.

2. **Contagious Expansion** Some cultural traits are adopted by people to whom they did not originally belong. Typically, this occurs because people are exposed to and adopt the trait (thus the term contagious expansion). Food provides good examples. For example, immigrants bring their cuisines to the United States, and Americans try them. Tandoori chicken (India), quesadillas (Mexico), and couscous (North Africa) have been adopted by Americans.

3. **Hierarchical Diffusion** When a cultural trait starts in a large city, is picked up in other large cities, and then slowly spreads to small cities, towns, and rural areas, it is spreading by hierarchical diffusion. Music styles, fashions, and slang are examples of traits that diffuse in this way.

The diffusion of a culture or trait can be stopped by physical or social barriers. Physical barriers include oceans, mountains, and deserts. In the past, physical barriers isolated people more than they do today. Modern transportation and communication have made physical barriers less important. Social barriers such as differences in language, religion, race, ethnicity, and historical enmity still slow cultural diffusion.

Geography Practice 2

Choose the <u>one best answer</u> to each question.

1. According to the passage, what do all cultures have?

   (1) universal categories of traits
   (2) large populations of members
   (3) more than one religion
   (4) physical barriers against other cultures
   (5) a history of aggression

2. What is cultural diffusion?

   (1) the weakening of a culture or cultural trait
   (2) the domination of one culture over another
   (3) the changing and spreading of a culture or cultural trait
   (4) the isolation of a culture in a physically remote area
   (5) the migration of a group of people from one area to another

3. When India won its independence in 1947, it adopted English, the language of its colonial rulers, as its official language, even though most Indians spoke hundreds of different native languages.

   What was the most likely reason that English became India's official language?

   (1) English favored no particular ethnic group and provided a means of communication that everyone could use.
   (2) Using English would make adopting other British cultural traits much easier.
   (3) English is the most widely used language on Earth, especially in North America and Australia.
   (4) English is the language of international trade and the Internet.
   (5) English is easier to learn than India's native languages.

4. When the Spanish settled the American Southwest, they brought the Spanish language, Catholicism, and Spanish laws and customs with them. What is this an example of?

   (1) a cultural trait
   (2) cultural diffusion through migration
   (3) cultural diffusion through contagious expansion
   (4) cultural diffusion through hierarchical diffusion
   (5) a physical barrier that stopped cultural diffusion

Question 5 refers to the following table.

Immigrant Populations in Central America, 2002

Nation	Total population	Immigrant population	Percent of total
Belize	226,000	17,000	7.5
Costa Rica	4,024,000	311,000	7.4
El Salvador	6,278,000	24,000	0.4
Guatemala	11,385,000	43,000	0.4
Honduras	6,417,000	44,000	0.7
Mexico	98,872,000	521,000	0.5
Nicaragua	5,071,000	27,000	0.5
Panama	2,856,000	82,000	2.9

Source: United Nations Population Division

5. Which of the following questions can be answered by consulting the table?

   (1) Where do immigrants to Central America come from?
   (2) Which Central American nation has the fastest growing immigrant population?
   (3) How many people emigrate from Central America to the United States?
   (4) Which Central American nation has the most immigrants from the United States?
   (5) Which Central American nation has the largest percentage of immigrants?

Answers and explanations start on page 89.

People and the Environment

People choose places to live based on their geographical advantages. In the ancient world, most of the early civilizations developed in river valleys where water was available for drinking, irrigation, and transportation (see page 14). Today a person might choose a place to live based on its nearness to a major highway or city. When people settle in an area, they change it in many ways. Agriculture transforms the landscape, as do towns, cities, suburbs, roads, dams, railroads, and industry.

Important Resources

People also change the environment by using Earth's resources in all their activities. A resource is anything that people find useful. The most basic resources are air, water, and the land itself—used for agriculture, industry, and settlement. Beyond these basics are mineral resources such as iron, lead, and diamonds; plant resources such as timber; ocean resources, such as fish; and fossil fuel resources such as petroleum, coal, and natural gas. Note that culture influences what people consider a resource. In the United States, gasoline and oil are important energy resources because much of our machinery runs on these fuels. In contrast, in much of Africa, firewood is a more important energy resource than gasoline and oil.

Distribution of Resources

The distribution of natural resources is uneven. For example, about two-thirds of the world's petroleum reserves are located in the Middle East. Since petroleum is needed by all of the developing and developed nations, the countries that have it are economically and politically powerful. In the future, as the need for petroleum continues to grow and it becomes scarcer, the Middle Eastern countries will remain powerful. The scarcity and cost of petroleum and pollution from burning it have helped spur development of alternate sources of energy. These sources, such as solar power, wind power, geothermal power, and waterpower, are also unevenly distributed. However, they are renewable, an advantage they have over petroleum, of which there is a limited supply.

Another important resource that is unevenly distributed is fresh water. In some areas, water is so plentiful that it is used to generate electricity as well as for drinking, industry, and agriculture. In other areas, water is needed where it does not exist naturally. For example, in California, most of the rain falls on the northern part of the state, but demand for water is highest in the dry southern part of the state. Much of the water is captured in reservoirs and then delivered to southern California by canals, aqueducts, and pipelines. In southern California, about 80 percent of the water is used for agriculture. The rest is used by homes and industry. California, like many other western states, also draws water from the Colorado River. The limited supply of water in the American West, which is a naturally arid region with a fast growing population, has led to conflict among states and cities for the right to draw water from rivers, water supply systems, and underground aquifers.

Geography Practice 3

Choose the <u>one best answer</u> to each question.

1. According to the passage, what are the most basic natural resources?

   (1) oceans
   (2) land, water, and air
   (3) metals and other minerals
   (4) timber
   (5) energy resources

2. Why is the distribution of water a problem in California?

   (1) The system of canals, aqueducts, and tunnels is outdated.
   (2) The quality of the water decreases with the distance from its source.
   (3) Most rain falls into reservoirs all over the state.
   (4) Farms in southern California need water, but the north gets the most rain.
   (5) There is too much rainfall in northern California.

3. The development of technology is an example of cultural change that influences how resources are valued. Which of the following resources became more important soon after the Industrial Revolution began?

   (1) air
   (2) land
   (3) fish
   (4) fossil fuels
   (5) renewable resources

4. If people found a good substitute for petroleum, what would happen to the nations of the Middle East?

   (1) They would become industrialized.
   (2) Their political and economic power would decrease.
   (3) Their political and economic power would increase.
   (4) Their supply of petroleum would decrease.
   (5) Their supply of petroleum would increase.

5. The use of one resource can lead to the pollution or destruction of another. For example, strip mining can destroy the landscape and the soil. In the United States, what is the basis for deciding to use a resource even if another will be ruined?

   (1) the economic value of each resource
   (2) the natural beauty of each resource
   (3) the cultural diffusion of each resource
   (4) the renewability of the resources
   (5) whether or not the resources are basic

<u>Questions 6 and 7</u> refer to this map.

Natural Resources of Ukraine

6. According to the map, where is hydroelectric power produced in Ukraine?

   (1) on the Black Sea
   (2) on the Dnepr River
   (3) in Kharkov
   (4) in Odessa
   (5) north of Lvov

7. Is Ukraine likely to pursue the development of alternative fuels in the near future?

   (1) Yes, it has a good supply of iron.
   (2) No, it has many fossil fuel deposits.
   (3) Yes, it lacks large deposits of uranium.
   (4) No, it doesn't have enough manganese.
   (5) Yes, its only port is on the Black Sea.

Answers and explanations start on page 89.

Definition

On the GED Social Studies Test, you will be asked questions that require you to show that you understand what you read. To answer these comprehension questions, you will have to:

- select a summary statement
- identify a restatement of an idea
- recognize an implication

Sample Question

The Harappan civilization of the Indus River Valley flourished for a thousand years. The Harappans developed irrigation and grew wheat and cotton.

They built large cities, which were centers of trade. Indus objects have been found as far away as Sumer. And jade from China has been found at Harappan sites.

Around 1500 B.C., the Harappan civilization began to decline. There was severe flooding at Mohenjo-Daro, a major city. Then the climate became drier and the region became a near-desert. In addition, nomadic Aryan tribes invaded. Eventually, the Harappan civilization disappeared.

Which of the following best summarizes the passage?

(1) The Harappan civilization was located in the Indus Valley.
(2) The Harappans built large cities and irrigation systems but were invaded by Aryan tribes.
(3) The Harappans left many works of art, including poetry.
(4) The Harappan civilization flourished in the Indus River Valley for a thousand years and then began to decline around 1500 B.C.
(5) Around 1500 B.C., several factors combined to cause the decline of the Harappan civilization of the Indus River Valley.

Think It Through

Q: What is the passage about?
A: The passage is about the Harappan civilization of the Indus Valley.

Q: What is the question asking?
A: The question is asking for a summary of the passage—a brief restatement of the main points.

Q: Which choice is the best summary?
A: Choice 1 is a detail, not a main point or summary.
Choice 2 contains several details but omits some main points.
Choice 3 is not true, and it is not stated in the passage.
Choice 4 has the main points: Harappans lived in the Indus Valley for many years; the civilization declined around 1500 B.C.
Choice 5 contains only one of the two main points of the passage.

Answer and Explanation

(4) The Harappan civilization flourished in the Indus River Valley for a thousand years and then began to decline around 1500 B.C. This is the best summary because it contains the two main points of the passage.

Guided Practice

Questions 1–3 are based on the passage below. Use the hints to help you answer the questions. Explain why you chose each answer.

In 1800, France closed the port of New Orleans to American farmers, and President Thomas Jefferson became concerned about French control of the Mississippi River. Jefferson offered France $2 million for New Orleans. Instead, discouraged by a slave rebellion and deadly diseases in Haiti, France offered to sell all of the Louisiana Territory—from New Orleans north to Canada and west into the Rockies—for $15 million. The Louisiana Purchase doubled the size of the United States.

HINT: What is the topic of the passage?

1. Which of the following would be the best title for this passage?

   (1) The French Empire in America
   (2) Trading Rights on the Mississippi River
   (3) The Louisiana Purchase
   (4) The Sale of New Orleans
   (5) Thomas Jefferson and the French

   Answer _____ is correct because _____

   _____

   _____

HINT: Scan the passage to find the description of French actions against the U.S. How did Jefferson respond?

2. What did Jefferson do to counter the French threat to U.S. trade?

   (1) He declared war on France.
   (2) He offered to buy New Orleans.
   (3) He helped the French put down the slave revolt in Haiti.
   (4) He opened the port of New Orleans by force.
   (5) He enlisted the help of Haiti on the Mississippi River.

   Answer _____ is correct because _____

   _____

   _____

HINT: Consider the troubles France had with Haiti and might have in the future with Louisiana.

3. Which of the following is suggested by the fact that France offered to sell the Louisiana Territory after the Haitian slave revolt?

   (1) France wanted to settle Haitian slaves in Louisiana.
   (2) The purchase price of Louisiana was a bargain.
   (3) Spain was threatening to retake Louisiana Territory.
   (4) The first American offer for New Orleans was accepted.
   (5) France thought an empire in North America was too hard to run.

   Answer _____ is correct because _____

   _____

   _____

Answers and explanations start on page 90.

Choose the <u>one best answer</u> to each question.

1. The president can veto a bill passed by Congress by refusing to sign it and sending it back within ten days. Congress can then override the veto with a two-thirds vote in favor of the bill. If Congress has fewer than ten days left in session, the president can use a pocket veto: the president simply doesn't sign the bill and doesn't return it to Congress.

Which of the following is implied by the information about the pocket veto?

THINK: What happens to a bill after a pocket veto?

(1) Presidents frequently use pocket vetoes.
(2) A pocket veto can occur at any time.
(3) The president can use a pocket veto only once.
(4) A pocket veto can be overturned by a majority vote.
(5) Congress cannot override a pocket veto.

2. To make wise decisions about their purchases, consumers need information. When choosing a product, consumers should know what brands are available, the features offered by each brand's product, the quality of the various products, and their prices. With sufficient and accurate information, consumers can make good purchasing decisions that maximize value.

Which of the following is the best title for this passage?

THINK: What is the topic of the paragraph?

(1) Maximizing Value
(2) Buying and Selling Goods
(3) The Role of Information in Consumer Choices
(4) Brand Names and Quality
(5) Comparing Product Features, Prices, and Quality

Questions 3 and 4 refer to the following graph.

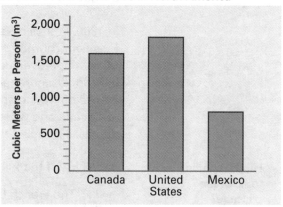

Annual Fresh Water Use in North America

Source: World Resources Institute

3. Approximately how many cubic meters (m^3) of water are used per person per year in the United States?

THINK: Which bar represents the amount of water used in the United States?

(1) 500 m^3
(2) 800 m^3
(3) 1,600 m^3
(4) 1,800 m^3
(5) 2,000 m^3

4. Which of the following best summarizes the data on this graph?

THINK: How do the amounts of fresh water use compare among these countries?

(1) The United States has more fresh water than Canada and Mexico.
(2) Mexicans use the least water per person.
(3) Americans use the most water per person.
(4) Canadians and Americans use approximately the same amount of water per person.
(5) Canadians and Americans use about twice as much water per person as Mexicans do.

Charles I became king of England in 1625. He firmly believed in the divine right of kings. When England's law-making body, Parliament, refused to give him money, he dissolved the legislature. However, in 1628, Charles needed a lot of money so he called Parliament into session. Parliament forced him to sign the Petition of Right. In this document, Charles promised not to levy taxes without Parliament's consent. He promised not to jail people without cause, nor to house soldiers in homes without consent. In return, Parliament gave him money.

Charles immediately dismissed Parliament and did not call it into session for 11 years. He also ignored the Petition of Right. But in 1640 Charles again needed money, this time to fight the Scots. He called Parliament into session. Before granting Charles money, Parliament had two of Charles's ministers tried and executed for abuse of power. As Parliament continued to meet, criticism of the king's abuses grew. Eventually Parliament condemned him as a tyrant. In retaliation, Charles had some members of Parliament arrested. This use of force made negotiating impossible. Both the king and Parliament began to raise armies, and the English Civil War started in 1642.

5. How did King Charles I limit the power of Parliament?

   (1) He asked Parliament for money.
   (2) He signed the Petition of Right.
   (3) He chose his ministers from members of Parliament.
   (4) He did not call Parliament into session for long periods of time.
   (5) He fought an invasion by the Scots.

6. Which is the best title for this passage?

   (1) The Divine Right of Kings
   (2) The English Monarchy
   (3) The Petition of Right
   (4) The Role of Parliament in the 1600s
   (5) Causes of the English Civil War

7. Based on the passage, what does the phrase *the divine right of kings* imply?

   (1) The king has absolute power.
   (2) The king must cooperate with Parliament.
   (3) The king must ask Parliament for money.
   (4) The king must defend the nation.
   (5) The king's power comes from the people.

Question 8 refers to the following information and photograph.

In the late 1800s and the early 1900s, factory wages in the United States were low. Workers often did not earn enough to support a family. Families sometimes took in piecework to make extra money, as shown in the photo below.

George Eastman House.

8. What do the information and the photograph imply about work at that time?

   (1) Both fathers and mothers were employed at factories.
   (2) Young children as well as parents contributed to the family income.
   (3) Most income came from doing piecework at home.
   (4) Working conditions were unhealthy.
   (5) Workers struck for higher wages.

Answers and explanations start on page 90.

Definition

On the GED Social Studies Test, you will be asked questions that require you to apply information to another situation. To answer these application questions, you will have to:

● identify a specific example of a generalization, principle, process, or idea
● apply information in a new situation or to a different context

Sample Question

Article IV, Section 2, of the U.S. Constitution formerly stated: *No person held to Service or Labour in one State, under the Laws thereof, escaping into another, shall in Consequence of any Law or Regulation therein, be discharged from such Service or Labour, but shall be delivered up on Claim of the Party to whom such Service or Labour may be due.*

This provision was struck down in 1865 when Amendment XIII, which abolished slavery, was ratified.

In which situation would the above provision of Article IV, Section 2, apply?

(1) In 1825, an apprentice breaks his contract with his Philadelphia employer and hides in Philadelphia.
(2) In 1845, a runaway slave from Virginia is captured in Ohio.
(3) In 1876, a cook quits his job in Maine and travels to Vermont.
(4) In 1925, three servants are convicted of conspiring to defraud their employer in Missouri.
(5) In 1996, groups of convicted prisoners clean highways in Utah.

Think It Through

Q: What is the main idea of the passage?
A: According to Article IV, runaway slaves and indentured servants captured in one state had to be returned to their masters in another state, until slavery was abolished by Amendment XIII.

Q: What is the question asking?
A: The question is asking you to identify a situation in which Article IV, Section 2, would apply.

Q: Which choice is the best illustration of this?
A: Choice 1 involves only one state, so it does not apply.
Choice 2 is a situation in which Article IV, Section 2, applies.
Choice 3 takes place after 1865, so it does not apply.
Choice 4 takes place after 1865, so it does not apply.
Choice 5 takes place after 1865, so it does not apply.

Answer and Explanation

(2) In 1845, a runaway slave from Virginia is captured in Ohio. This is the best example because it takes place while Article IV, Section 2, was still in force (before 1865) and it involves two states.

Guided Practice

Question 1 is based on the passage below. Use the hint to help you answer the question. Use the lines to explain why you chose your answer.

Corporations can pay for their activities in several ways. First, they can finance activities themselves by spending some of their profits. Second, they can borrow money from a financial institution such as a bank or an insurance company. Third, corporations can sell stock, or shares of ownership, to the public. And finally, corporations can issue bonds to be purchased by investors.

HINT: The company is borrowing to buy a building. What consumer activity is most like this?

1. Best Corporation borrows money from a bank to fund the purchase of a warehouse. To which consumer situation is this most similar?

    (1) A student uses a debit card to buy textbooks.
    (2) A shopper uses a credit card to buy party goods.
    (3) A couple takes out a mortgage to buy their first house.
    (4) A family budgets a portion of their income to repay a loan.
    (5) A worker is paid by electronic transfer to her checking account.

    Answer _____ is correct because _____

    _____

Question 2 is based on the passage below. As before, use the hint to help you answer the question, and explain your answer choice.

Geographers classify economic activities into four groups. Primary activities—such as farming, mining, and fishing—directly involve land, oceans, or bodies of fresh water. Secondary activities—such as processing or manufacturing—change raw materials to make them more valuable. Tertiary activities—such as retailing and banking—involve the provision of goods and services. And quaternary activities involve research, information processing, and administration.

HINT: Look for an activity that involves changing a raw material into something with added value.

2. Which is an example of a secondary economic activity?

    (1) A cheese maker makes cheddar cheese from milk.
    (2) A dentist fills the cavities in a child's teeth.
    (3) A geography professor investigates local climate change.
    (4) A lumberman fells a large tree.
    (5) A prospector pans for gold.

    Answer _____ is correct because _____

    _____

Answers and explanations start on page 90.

Choose the <u>one best answer</u> to each question.

1. In the 1300s, an epidemic of the bubonic plague swept through Europe and killed about one-third of the population. The plague destroyed social and economic structures throughout the continent.

Which is most similar to the experience of Europe with the bubonic plague?

THINK: Look for a situation in which an epidemic affects social and economic stability.

(1) the present African AIDS epidemic, which has killed thousands of adults and orphaned their children
(2) the SARS epidemic of 2003, which killed hundreds of people, mostly in Asia
(3) polio, which was controlled by the use of the Salk vaccine in the late 1900s
(4) Legionnaires' disease, which had several local outbreaks in the late 1900s
(5) the common cold, which many people throughout the world suffer through seasonally, but which is rarely fatal

2. In 1954, the U.S. Supreme Court ruled in *Brown* v. *Board of Education of Topeka* that segregated schools were unequal. This ruling spurred the civil rights movement, which highlighted the injustices to which African Americans were subjected. Its main goal was to help African Americans gain equal treatment under the law.

Which of the following is another example of a group pressing for civil rights?

THINK: What is the key characteristic of civil rights?

(1) the National Coalition for Disability Rights defending the right of disabled Americans to fair and equal treatment
(2) Greenpeace's demonstrations to protect the environment
(3) AARP's pressing for Social Security and Medicare changes to benefit seniors
(4) Common Cause's advocacy of political reform
(5) Mobil Oil's ads promoting the oil industry

Questions 3 and 4 refer to the following table.

Criminal versus Civil Trials

	Criminal trial	Civil trial
Who brings the suit (the plaintiff)?	Government	Private individual or group
Who is the defendant?	Accused criminal	Private individual or group
What type of wrongdoing took place?	A violation of the criminal code	Harm to a private individual or group
What is the outcome?	Decision on guilt and punishment	Decision on guilt and compensation

3. O. J. Simpson was charged by the state of California with the murder of his ex-wife and found not guilty. Which type of trial was this?

THINK: What was the offense?

(1) a criminal trial, because Simpson was the defendant
(2) a criminal trial, because murder is a crime and California was the plaintiff
(3) a criminal trial, because Simpson was acquitted
(4) a civil trial, because Simpson was a private individual
(5) a civil trial, because there was a decision on guilt

4. Simpson's former in-laws filed suit against him, seeking to be paid for the pain and suffering caused by his ex-wife's death. They won. Which type of trial was this?

THINK: Who were the parties to the suit?

(1) a criminal trial, since murder is a crime
(2) a criminal trial, because Simpson was acquitted in the trial brought by the state
(3) a criminal trial, because it was found that Simpson caused pain and suffering
(4) a civil trial, because it was a matter between private individuals
(5) a civil trial, because it was handled by a government judge

5. A sin tax is a tax on a specific product. Its purpose is to discourage consumption of the product, as well as raise money in the public interest. Which of the following is a sin tax?

(1) income tax
(2) sales tax
(3) cigarette tax
(4) property tax
(5) value added tax

Questions 6–9 refer to the following information.

Many factors explain why cities are founded at particular sites. Among them are:

Agricultural potential: large amount of relatively level land along with adequate rain, run-off, or another fresh water supply.
Protected harbor: calm, sheltered water in which to load and unload ships.
Head of navigation: the farthest location up a river that a boat can travel.
Confluence of two rivers: a place where two rivers meet to form a larger river.
Defense: a site easily defended from attack because of its geography.

6. Los Angeles, California, was settled by the Spanish because the site had fresh water flowing down from the nearby mountains and ample flat land suitable for growing crops. Which factor played a major role in the siting of Los Angeles?

(1) agricultural potential
(2) protected harbor
(3) head of navigation
(4) confluence of two rivers
(5) defense

7. Trenton, New Jersey, is located on the Delaware River where the water is just deep enough for sizable boats to navigate. Which factor played a major role in its siting?

(1) agricultural potential
(2) protected harbor
(3) head of navigation
(4) confluence of two rivers
(5) defense

8. Paris, France, began on the Ile de la Cite, a very small island in the Seine River. Which factor played a major role in the siting of Paris?

(1) agricultural potential
(2) protected harbor
(3) head of navigation
(4) confluence of two rivers
(5) defense

9. Pittsburgh, Pennsylvania, began as a small settlement where the Allegheny and Monongahela rivers flow together, forming the Ohio River. Which factor played a major role in its siting?

(1) agricultural potential
(2) protected harbor
(3) head of navigation
(4) confluence of two rivers
(5) defense

Question 10 refers to the following photograph.

© John Van Hasselt/CORBIS

10. Which situation is most similar to the scene shown in the photograph?

(1) Chilean fruit being sold in U.S. stores
(2) a French fast-food chain becoming established in the United States
(3) the movement to promote organic farming
(4) the movement to increase public transportation
(5) genetically modified food being developed in laboratories

Answers and explanations start on page 90.

Definition

Some questions on the GED Social Studies Test will ask you to analyze information. You will have to examine relationships among ideas. To answer these analysis questions, you will have to:

- identify cause and effect
- distinguish fact from opinion
- figure out the most likely reason for something
- recognize unstated assumptions
- recognize information that is designed to persuade
- compare and contrast points of view or ideas

Sample Question

The nation's highest court is the Supreme Court. The Supreme Court hears cases involving ambassadors and consuls; it also hears cases in which any state is a party. Finally, parties involved in any case tried in federal appellate courts can submit their case to the Supreme Court. The nine Supreme Court justices (judges) have the sole authority to decide which cases to review. Congress sets the number of Supreme Court justices. The first Supreme Court had six justices; a few decades later the number was set a ten. In 1869, Congress set the number of justices at nine—the number we have today.

What is the most likely reason the number of Supreme Court justices has been constant for more than a century?

(1) The justices need to divide the lower courts among themselves.
(2) The justices can decide whether to hear cases involving ambassadors.
(3) This number makes it possible for a majority ruling on any case.
(4) This number allows justices holding minority opinions to hear cases.
(5) This number is specified by the states.

Think It Through

Q: What is the passage about?
A: It describes kinds of cases the Supreme Court hears and the number of justices the Supreme Court has had.

Q: What is the question asking?
A: It is asking why the number of Supreme Court justices changed early in the Court's history but has remained at nine for many decades.

Q: Which choice is the most likely reason?
A: Choice 1 is incorrect because the justices don't preside over these courts. Choice 2 is incorrect because the justices do not oversee these courts. **Choice 3 is correct; there is less likely to be an even split on a decision if all nine justices vote.** Choice 4 is incorrect because all of the justices hear cases. Choice 5 is incorrect because Congress, not the states, sets the number.

Answer and Explanation

(3) This number makes it possible for a majority ruling on any case. With all justices voting, there will always be a clear majority.

Guided Practice

Questions 1 and 2 are based on the passage below. Use the hints to help you answer the questions. Explain why you chose each answer.

Dred Scott, a slave from Missouri, was taken to the free territory of Wisconsin, where he lived for two years. When he returned to Missouri, Scott sued for his freedom. He claimed that living in Wisconsin had made him a free man. Scott lost the case but appealed it to the Supreme Court. In *Dred Scott* v. *Sandford* (1857), the Court ruled against Scott. The justices argued that slaves were a form of property and that Congress did not have the power to deprive citizens of their property. In effect, they claimed, Congress could not forbid slavery in any new territory. The Court declared that Congress's 1820 law, the Missouri Compromise, was unconstitutional. This law had excluded slavery from new northern territories while permitting it in the new southern territories.

HINT: Reread the sentences that explain the logic behind the Court's decision.

1. What assumption underlay the Supreme Court's reasoning in the *Dred Scott* decision?

   (1) Wisconsin could not be declared a slave territory.
   (2) Slaves were not U.S. citizens, so they were not protected as citizens under the law.
   (3) Property rights were less important than human rights when slavery was involved.
   (4) Congress should not make any laws regarding slavery.
   (5) Slavery was morally wrong and should be abolished.

   Answer _____ is correct because _____

   _____

   _____

HINT: Which region would become more powerful if all new territories were slave territories?

2. The Missouri Compromise had helped maintain the balance of power between northern and southern states. How did the North and South most likely react to the *Dred Scott* decision?

   (1) Both the North and the South favored the decision.
   (2) Both the North and the South opposed the decision.
   (3) The North favored the decision, and the South opposed it.
   (4) The North opposed the decision, and the South favored it.
   (5) Both the North and the South were against the Court overturning any Congressional law.

   Answer _____ is correct because _____

   _____

   _____

Answers and explanations start on page 90.

Choose the <u>one best answer</u> to each question.

1. One way that businesses have blocked competition is to own an essential resource. For example, the Aluminum Company of America was a monopoly for many years because it controlled the world's supply of bauxite—the ore used to make aluminum.

   What might happen if a company lost its monopoly over a resource?

   THINK: What would happen if other companies had access to the resource?

   (1) The company would become more powerful.
   (2) Other firms would become bankrupt.
   (3) Other firms would enter the industry.
   (4) The supply of the resource would increase.
   (5) The supply of the resource would quickly run out.

2. The country of Namibia, in Africa, is very hot and dry. The Namib Desert stretches from the Atlantic coast to the great central plateau. The Kalahari Desert covers most of the central plateau. To the north is an area of savanna with varied wildlife including elephants, giraffes, and lions. This region gets a little seasonal rainfall.

   What is a likely economic effect of Namibia's climate?

   THINK: What is affected by hot, dry weather?

   (1) The climate stimulates economic development in the plateau region.
   (2) Agriculture is difficult, and food must be imported.
   (3) Most people make a living from vegetable farming.
   (4) Manufacturing is the main economic activity.
   (5) Domesticating the native wildlife is an important occupation.

Question 3 refers to the following information and cartoon.

During the Age of Imperialism, Belgium ruled the Congo. In fact, King Leopold of Belgium treated the Congo as his personal property from 1885 to 1908. This cartoon from 1906 shows a critical view of King Leopold's behavior.

IN THE RUBBER COILS.

3. What aspect of the cartoon does the most to persuade the reader that Leopold exploited the Congo?

   THINK: What is Leopold doing?

   (1) Leopold has no arms.
   (2) Leopold is wearing a crown.
   (3) The woman and child are escaping.
   (4) The man is muscular.
   (5) Leopold is squeezing the man.

Questions 4 and 5 refer to the following information.

Historians have had different views of why the United States entered World War I. Soon after the war, many historians criticized President Wilson's policies. They argued that Wilson was really pro-British even while the United States was neutral. They claim Wilson went to war because U.S. businesses would profit. Later, after World War II had begun, views of Wilson began to change. Some historians began to view the U.S. entry into World War I as an inevitable response to German submarine attacks on ships, including passenger ships, crossing the Atlantic. In these attacks, dozens of Americans died. In this view, Wilson was a strong president who responded appropriately to the violation of U.S. neutrality.

4. Which of the following is an opinion rather than a fact?

   (1) Wilson was president at the time of World War I.
   (2) The United States was neutral at the beginning of World War I.
   (3) German submarines attacked passenger ships.
   (4) American citizens were killed while sailing across the Atlantic.
   (5) Wilson was a gifted leader who did the right thing by entering World War I.

5. How does the later interpretation of Wilson's actions compare to the immediate postwar interpretation?

   (1) The later interpretation is much more favorable to Wilson.
   (2) The later interpretation focuses on Wilson's character, not his actions.
   (3) The later interpretation emphasizes Wilson's economic reasons for entering the war.
   (4) The later interpretation criticizes Wilson for his actions regarding the war.
   (5) The later interpretation compares Wilson to his British counterpart.

Question 6 refers to the following information and chart.

Most Americans who are registered to vote usually vote. Nonvoters have many reasons for not voting.

Most Common Reasons for Not Voting

Reason	Percentage
Did not register	42%
Do not like the candidates	17%
No particular reason	10%
Sick or disabled	8%
Not a U.S. citizen	5%
Not interested in politics	5%
Cannot make it to polls	4%
Other reasons	9%

6. Given this information, what would be the most effective way to get more people to vote?

   (1) Make registration more convenient.
   (2) Put better candidates in the races.
   (3) Allow the sick and disabled to vote from home.
   (4) Streamline the naturalization process.
   (5) Make politics more interesting.

7. A sole proprietorship is a business run by one person. A self-employed appliance repairer and a freelance computer programmer are examples of sole proprietorships.

   Which is the most likely reason that sole proprietorships account for only tiny portion of total business sales?

   (1) They are more common than other forms of business organization.
   (2) They are inexpensive to start up.
   (3) The proprietor keeps the profits.
   (4) They are typically very small.
   (5) Their products are inexpensive.

Answers and explanations start on page 90.

Definition

On the GED Social Studies Test, you will be asked questions that require you to make judgments. To answer these evaluation questions, you will have to:

- decide whether information supports a point of view or a conclusion
- determine which question can be answered with particular information
- identify fallacies in reasoning or logic
- recognize the role that values play in decision making

Sample Question

In 1798, Thomas Malthus wrote an essay on population. In it, he stated that the world's population was growing far faster than the food supply. Malthus predicted that this imbalance would lead to widespread famine and disaster unless the birthrate was reduced. At the time of Malthus's essay, agricultural yields were low and transportation of food was limited. There were no immediate prospects for improving food supply or distribution. Since his time, however, the use of nitrogen-based fertilizers and other improvements in technology and transportation have increased productivity. Despite a falling birthrate in the developed world, the world's population has grown far beyond what Malthus thought it could sustain.

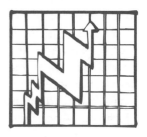

Malthus's prediction of worldwide famine has not come to pass. What was wrong with his reasoning?

(1) He did not predict a decline in world population.
(2) He did not foresee the spread of birth control methods.
(3) He did not believe that people could reduce the birthrate.
(4) He did not see that increased population means more farmers.
(5) He did not anticipate that the food supply would increase.

Think It Through

Q: What is the passage about?
A: It explains Malthus's predictions about population growth.

Q: What is the question asking?
A: It is asking why Malthus's predictions have not come true.

Q: Which choice explains what was wrong with Malthus's reasoning?
A: Choice 1 is incorrect because total population has grown.
Choice 2 is incorrect because, despite the availability of birth control, the world population has climbed steadily.
Choice 3 is incorrect because the birthrate has fallen in some places.
Choice 4 is incorrect because more farmers did not account for the increases in food supply.
Choice 5 is correct because Malthus assumed that agricultural techniques would remain as they were in 1798.

Answer and Explanation

(5) He did not anticipate that the food supply would increase. Fertilizers and machinery have improved agricultural productivity.

Guided Practice

Question 1 is based on the passage below. Use the hint to help you answer the question. Explain why you chose your answer.

Between 1807 and 1812, Napoleon Bonaparte ruled an empire extending from France to the border of Russia. He himself was emperor of France and the Netherlands. He made his brother Joseph king of Spain. Other states had to follow Napoleon's policies. Soon, opposition to Napoleon's rule grew. Conquered peoples resented paying taxes to France and serving in its army. Revolts broke out all over Europe as people tried to restore their own governments, traditions, and customs.

HINT: Think about how people feel when a foreign country takes over their country.

1. What did Europeans show they valued by rebelling against Napoleon?

   (1) democracy
   (2) law and order
   (3) equal rights
   (4) national identity
   (5) French culture

   Answer _____ is correct because _____

   _____

   _____

Question 2 is based on the passage below. As before, use the hint to help you answer the question, and explain your answer choice.

The Great Depression began in the United States with the collapse of the stock market in 1929. Many people, including President Herbert Hoover, thought that prosperity would soon return. However, it soon became apparent that the depression was deepening and spreading. One of Hoover's first actions was to approve the Hawley-Smoot Tariff in 1930. This law raised tariffs on imported goods in an attempt to protect U.S. businesses from foreign competition. In return, European nations placed higher tariffs on American goods. The effect was to reduce trade for all.

HINT: Think about what happens to businesses when they lose a portion of their market.

2. What information supports the conclusion that the Hawley-Smoot Tariff made the worldwide economic depression worse?

   (1) Signing the tariff into law was one of Hoover's first actions.
   (2) The law raised tariffs on imported goods.
   (3) Tariffs protect a country's industries from competition.
   (4) European nations raised tariffs on U.S. goods in response.
   (5) Reduced international trade decreased economic activity.

   Answer _____ is correct because _____

   _____

   _____

Answers and explanations start on page 90.

Choose the <u>one best answer</u> to each question.

<u>Questions 1–3</u> refer to the following information.

Amendment VI of the Bill of Rights states in part:

In all criminal prosecutions, the accused shall enjoy the right to a speedy and public trial....

1. Which of the following did the drafters of this amendment value?

   THINK: What is guaranteed by this clause of the amendment?

   (1) openness in government proceedings
   (2) appropriate punishment for crimes
   (3) the right to privacy
   (4) freedom from searches of property
   (5) freedom from being tried twice for a crime

2. For which of the following positions could this clause be cited as support?

   THINK: Which position involves either speedy trials or public trials?

   (1) Criminal trials should be televised.
   (2) Repeat offenders of serious crimes should not be offered bail.
   (3) The death penalty should be abolished.
   (4) Search warrants should be obtained when a vehicle needs to be searched.
   (5) Accused criminals must take the witness stand at their trials.

3. The Progressive Movement arose in the early 1900s in reaction to political corruption in big-city political machines, the growing power of big business and monopolies, and the plight of the urban poor.

   Which of the following did the Progressives most likely value?

   THINK: What were people in the Progressive Movement fighting against?

   (1) the efficiency of large organizations
   (2) change for the sake of change
   (3) the welfare of ordinary people
   (4) loyalty to political officials
   (5) the rights of business owners

<u>Questions 4 and 5</u> refer to the following graph.

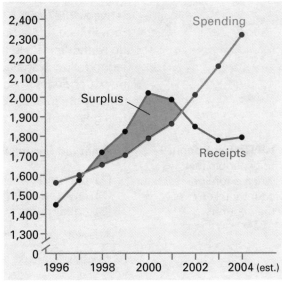

Federal Receipts and Spending, 1996–2004 (in billions of dollars)

Source: U.S. Office of Management and Budget

4. Which of the following questions can be answered by this graph?

   THINK: Do the data address this question?

   (1) What does the government spend money on?
   (2) Where do federal receipts come from?
   (3) When did the government have a budget surplus?
   (4) How much did the government spend on Social Security in 2000?
   (5) How much did the government spend in total in 2005?

5. What evidence supports the conclusion that there was a budget deficit in 2004?

   THINK: What do the 2004 data points show?

   (1) the difference between receipts and spending that year
   (2) increased federal spending each year
   (3) increased receipts from 1997 to 2000
   (4) decreased receipts from 2000 to 2003
   (5) the fact that 2004 figures are estimates

Question 6 refers to the following map.

6. Which of the following questions can be answered by the information on this map?

   (1) Which countries border Colombia?
   (2) At what latitude and longitude is Bogotá located?
   (3) Is Colombia a mountainous country?
   (4) What natural resources does Colombia have?
   (5) What is the fastest river in Colombia?

7. In the late 1800s, European nations and the United States expanded their power, taking over areas of Africa, Asia, and Latin America without provocation. Which argument could they have used to justify this imperialism?

   (1) Power should be divided among peoples of all continents.
   (2) All nations have the right to defend themselves.
   (3) The Western Hemisphere is off limits to European expansion.
   (4) War is a last resort after diplomacy.
   (5) In the political world, as in nature, only the strongest survive.

Questions 8 and 9 refer to the following information.

In October 1962, U.S. spy planes discovered that the Soviet Union was building nuclear missile sites in Cuba, just 90 miles from Florida. President Kennedy responded to this threat by blockading Cuba. If Soviet ships challenged the U.S. Navy, a nuclear war between the two superpowers seemed inevitable. After many tense days, Khrushchev agreed to remove the missiles in exchange for Kennedy's promise not to invade Cuba. Soon after, a telephone hotline was established between Washington and Moscow, so the nations' leaders could talk directly during a crisis.

8. Which of the following beliefs most likely contributed to the establishment of the communications hotline?

   (1) Arms control was necessary for the safety of the world.
   (2) Personal diplomacy would help solve international problems.
   (3) Only the superpowers should have had nuclear weapons.
   (4) Reliable communication between the superpowers was impossible.
   (5) Diplomacy required that a country inform another country about the intent to attack.

9. Which of the following questions can be answered by the information in the passage?

   (1) Why did Cuba permit the Soviet Union to build missile sites?
   (2) Were the missiles in Cuba ready to be launched?
   (3) How did President Kennedy counter the threat of missiles in Cuba?
   (4) Who did President Kennedy consult in deciding how to respond to the crisis?
   (5) What support did Khrushchev have in Moscow for his actions?

Answers and explanations start on page 91.

Definition

On the GED Social Studies Test, you will have to read and interpret information presented in graphs and charts. To answer questions based these graphics, you will have to:

* find and understand specific information or data
* interpret the information in the graph or chart
* determine the main idea of a graph or chart

Minority Representation in the House of Representatives, 1985–2003

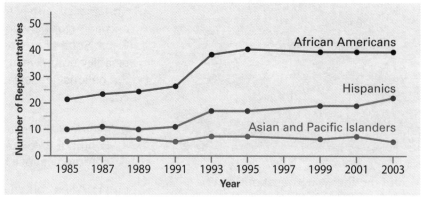

Source: U.S. Census Bureau, compiled from data in *Congressional Directory, biennial*

Sample Question

What do the trend lines suggest about African American and Hispanic representation in the House of Representatives from 1985 to 2003?

(1) Both groups tripled their numbers in the House.
(2) Both groups made slight increases in their representation.
(3) Both groups held steady in the number of representatives.
(4) Neither group increased its numbers in the House.
(5) African Americans increased their numbers, but Hispanics lost representatives.

Think It Through

Q: What does the graph show?
A: It shows the number of members from three minority groups in the House of Representatives from 1985 to 2003.

Q: What is the question asking?
A: It is asking for a generalization about African American and Hispanic membership in the House of Representative during this period.

Q: Which choice is correct?
A: Choice 1 is incorrect because the numbers doubled (approximately).
Choice 2 is correct; the trend lines move upward very gradually.
Choice 3 is contradicted by the upward sloping trend lines.
Choice 4 is incorrect because both groups increased their numbers.
Choice 5 is incorrect because both groups increased their numbers.

Answer and Explanation

(2) Both groups made slight increases in their representation. The trend lines for both African Americans and Hispanics rise gradually over time.

Guided Practice

Questions 1 and 2 are based on the graph below. Use the hints to help you answer the questions. Explain why you chose each answer.

Average Yearly Income of Married-Couple Families, 1980 and 2000 (in constant 2000 dollars)

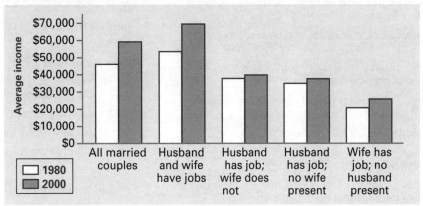

Source: U.S. Census Bureau

HINT: Look at the key to see what the 2000 bars look like. Then find the bar that represents 2000 income when both spouses work. Read across to the vertical axis to find the amount.

1. In 2000, approximately what was the average yearly income of a married-couple family in which both spouses worked?

   (1) $69,000
   (2) $59,000
   (3) $46,000
   (4) $39,000
   (5) $25,000

   Answer _____ is correct because _____

   _____

   _____

HINT: Test each generalization by checking it against the graph's data.

2. Which generalization is supported by the data in the graph?

   (1) Both spouses must work in order for a family to survive.
   (2) In general, income fell between 1980 and 2000.
   (3) After married couple families retire, their income decreases.
   (4) On average, wives earn less than husbands.
   (5) Married couple families earn more than single people.

   Answer _____ is correct because _____

   _____

   _____

Answers and explanations start on page 91.

Choose the <u>one best answer</u> to each question.

Questions 1 and 2 refer to this chart.

Geographic Data—The Philippines

Location	Southeastern Asia, between the Philippine Sea and the South China Sea
Land Area	300,000 square kilometers (7,107 islands)
Climate	tropical marine; in typhoon belt; struck by an average of six typhoons per year
Terrain	mostly mountains with narrow to extensive coastal lowlands
Natural Resources	timber, petroleum, nickel, cobalt, silver, gold, salt, copper
Population	86,241,697 (2004 est.)
Ethnic Groups	various Malay 95.5%, Chinese 1.5%, other 3%
Religions	Roman Catholic 84.1%, Philippine Independent Church 6.2%, Muslim 4.3%, Protestant 3.9%, Buddhist and others 1.5%
Official Languages	Filipino (based on Tagalog dialect) and English
Literacy	male 92.5%, female 92.7%
Government Type	multiparty republic with two legislative houses

Source: World Factbook, Central Intelligence Agency

1. What is the majority religion in the Philippines?

THINK: Which section of the chart shows religious groups?

(1) Roman Catholicism
(2) the Philippine Independent Church
(3) Islam
(4) Protestant Christianity
(5) Buddhism

2. What aspects of the Philippines' geography make the country vulnerable to weather disasters?

THINK: What type of weather would cause a disaster?

(1) its land area
(2) its tropical marine climate
(3) its location in the typhoon belt
(4) its natural resources
(5) its literacy rate

Questions 3 and 4 refer to this information and bar graph.

Americans get their news from various sources, as shown in the graph below. The percentages in the graph do not add up to 100% because many people use several different sources to learn the news.

Daily Sources of News, 2004

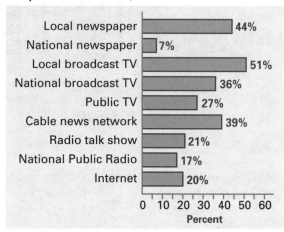

Source: The Gallup Poll, 2004

3. From which source do the fewest people get their daily news?

THINK: Read the percentages printed on the bars. Which is lowest?

(1) local newspapers   **(4)** talk radio
(2) national newspapers   **(5)** the Internet
(3) National Public Radio

4. Janice is the marketing director of a nationwide insurance company that wants to advertise a new financial product to people who follow current events. Which of the following media would give her the largest audience nationwide?

THINK: Compare the percentages for each of the following news sources and choose the highest.

(1) national broadcast TV
(2) public TV
(3) radio talk show
(4) National Public Radio
(5) the Internet

Questions 5–7 refer to these circle graphs.

**Occupations of Members
of Two State Assemblies, 1780s**

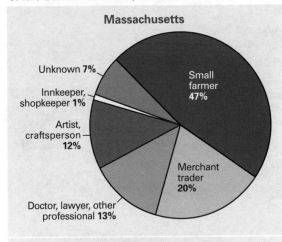

Massachusetts

Unknown 7%

Innkeeper,
shopkeeper 1%

Artist,
craftsperson
12%

Doctor, lawyer, other
professional 13%

Small
farmer
47%

Merchant
trader
20%

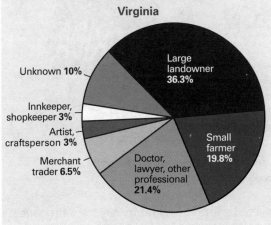

Virginia

Unknown 10%

Innkeeper,
shopkeeper 3%

Artist,
craftsperson 3%

Merchant
trader 6.5%

Large
landowner
36.3%

Doctor,
lawyer, other
professional
21.4%

Small
farmer
19.8%

Source: Jackson T. Main, *Political Parties Before the Constitution*

5. What percentage of the Massachusetts assembly were artists or craftspeople?

(1) 1%   (4) 13%
(2) 3%   (5) 20%
(3) 12%

6. What occupation did just under 20% of the Virginia assembly hold?

(1) doctor   (4) merchant
(2) innkeeper   (5) small farmer
(3) large landowner

7. What evidence from the graphs supports the conclusion that large plantations were more common in southern states like Virginia than in northern states like Massachusetts?

(1) the percentage of merchant/traders in Virginia compared to the percentage in Massachusetts
(2) the percentage of small farmers in Virginia compared to the percentage in Massachusetts
(3) the percentage of large landowners in Virginia compared to the percentage in Massachusetts
(4) the percentage of professionals in Virginia compared to the percentage in Massachusetts
(5) the percentage of innkeepers and shopkeepers in Virginia compared to the percentage in Massachusetts

Question 8 refers to this table.

**World Population, 1000–1900
(estimated population in millions)**

Continent	Year			
	1000	1700	1800	1900
Europe	36	120	180	390
Asia	185	415	625	970
Africa	33	61	70	110
the Americas	39	13	24	145
Oceania	2	2	3	7

Source: Population estimates by Dennis H. Wrong

8. Which region's population growth differs from the general pattern?

(1) Europe, because its population rose between 1800 and 1900
(2) Asia, because its population rose between 1700 and 1900
(3) Oceania, because its population rose between 1800 and 1900
(4) the Americas, because their population fell between 1000 and 1700 and then rose
(5) Africa, because its population rose between 1000 and 1700

Answers and explanations start on page 91.

Definition

On the GED Social Studies Test, you will have to read and interpret visual information presented in editorial cartoons and photographs. To answer questions based on cartoons and photos, you may have to:

- understand specific images and symbols
- determine the main idea of the cartoon or photo
- identify the cartoonist's or photographer's point of view

'THAT'S IT. WE'RE RETIRING TO NEBRASKA.'

© 2004 Jeff Koterba, Omaha World Herald NE.

Sample Question

The year this cartoon was published, Florida was hit by several hurricanes. Why is this cartoon couple moving to Nebraska?

(1) Nebraska is their home state.
(2) They have jobs in Nebraska.
(3) Their children live in Nebraska.
(4) They can't stand the heat.
(5) The storms are too severe.

Think It Through

Q: What does the cartoon show?
A: It shows a retired couple in a packed car leaving a stormy Florida.

Q: Which choice represents the reason why the couple is leaving Florida?
A: Choice 1 may be true, but it's not the reason shown in the cartoon.
Choice 2 is incorrect because the couple is retired.
Choice 3 may be true, but it's not the reason shown in the cartoon.
Choice 4 is incorrect; wind, not heat, is the problem in the cartoon.
Choice 5 is correct because Florida often has severe storms.

Answer and Explanation

(5) The storms are too severe. Many people retire to Florida because of the warm weather, but Florida is in a hurricane path and often has bad storms.

Guided Practice

<u>Questions 1 and 2</u> are based on the photograph below. Use the hints to help you answer the questions. Explain why you chose each answer.

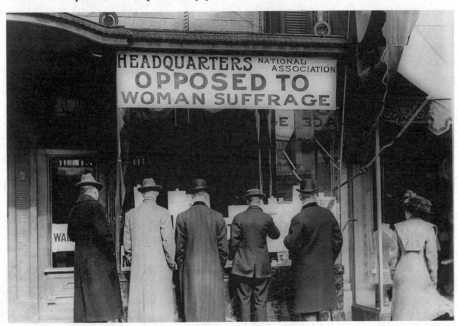

Library of Congress, Prints and Photographs, LC-USZ2-25338.

HINT: Read the sign over the storefront, and examine the row of people looking in.

1. What does this photograph suggest about the anti-suffragists—the opponents of women's right to vote?

   (1) The anti-suffragist movement was a local cause.
   (2) The anti-suffragist movement was very disorganized.
   (3) The anti-suffragists were fighting a losing battle.
   (4) Many anti-suffragists were poor.
   (5) Many anti-suffragists were men.

   Answer _____ is correct because _____

   _____

   _____

HINT: At that time, women's traditional role was primarily in the home and sometimes working factory jobs.

2. What belief about women did anti-suffragists likely hold?

   (1) Women should have equal rights under the law.
   (2) Women are equal to men in all aspects of life.
   (3) Women should focus their energy on family life.
   (4) Women should be encouraged to go to college.
   (5) Women will improve the world if they get the vote.

   Answer _____ is correct because _____

   _____

   _____

Answers and explanations start on page 91.

Choose the <u>one best answer</u> to each question.

<u>Questions 1 and 2</u> refer to the following information and cartoon.

The U.S. government influences the economy through its policies. This cartoon is commenting on a 2002 law that provides subsidies to the farm industry, which the government has been helping since the 1930s.

The Jolly Green Giant

© 2002, The Washington Post Writers Group. Reprinted with permission.

1. Who is the Jolly Green Giant?

   THINK: Read all the labels carefully.

   (1) the taxpayer
   (2) the farmer
   (3) Congress
   (4) the farm bill
   (5) the president

2. What image does the cartoonist use to persuade the reader that farmers make big financial gains from the farm bill?

   THINK: Look at each part of the picture carefully.

   (1) The Jolly Green Giant is carrying a pouch labeled "Farm Bill."
   (2) The Jolly Green Giant is tossing money for the farmer to catch.
   (3) The farmer is small.
   (4) The farm has several outbuildings.
   (5) There are rows of crops in the background.

<u>Questions 3 and 4</u> refer to the following photo.

© K. Hamilton/CORBIS/SYGMA

3. What form of political activity is shown?

   THINK: What are these people doing?

   (1) campaigning for a political candidate
   (2) raising funds for a political candidate
   (3) demonstrating for a cause
   (4) registering people to vote
   (5) striking for better health care

4. Which question can be answered by looking at the photograph?

   THINK: What does the photo actually show?

   (1) What group of people is in the photo?
   (2) What is the WTO?
   (3) Where is the activity taking place?
   (4) Did these people achieve their goal?
   (5) What other political activities do these people participate in?

Question 5 refers to the following information and photograph.

After 1945, East Berlin was communist and controlled by the Soviet Union; West Berlin was capitalist and controlled by the United States, Great Britain, and France. In the 1960s the Soviets built a wall dividing East and West Berlin to stop people from escaping to West Berlin for a freer, more prosperous life. The Berlin Wall stretched more than 103 miles and was heavily policed. In 1989, as the Soviet Union was losing its hold on Eastern Europe, the Berlin Wall was torn down.

© Regis Bossu/CORBIS/SYGMA

5. How did the attitude toward the Berlin Wall shown by the Germans in the photo most likely compare with the attitude of government leaders in the Soviet Union?

(1) Both the Germans and the Soviets saw the destruction of the Wall as a victory.

(2) Both the Germans and the Soviets saw the destruction of the Wall as a defeat.

(3) The Germans opposed the destruction of the Wall, and the Soviets favored it.

(4) The Germans favored the destruction of the Wall, and the Soviets opposed it.

(5) The Germans wanted to rebuild the Wall as a monument, and the Soviets wanted to rebuild it as a security measure.

Question 6 refers to this information and cartoon.

The Monroe Doctrine of 1823 set forth U.S. policy toward Latin America. It stated that the United States would oppose interference in the Americas. In 1823, the doctrine had little effect, but by 1900, when this cartoon appeared, it was the basis of U.S. foreign policy in Latin America.

EXPANSION!

© Bettmann/CORBIS

6. In this cartoon, Uncle Sam protects the Americas. What other interpretation is there of Uncle Sam's stance?

(1) South America is rising up against the United States.

(2) The United States has an imperial interest in Latin America.

(3) Democracy has spread in the Americas.

(4) Europe no longer threatens the Americas.

(5) Threats to the United States come from the north.

Answers and explanations start on page 91.

Definition

On the GED Social Studies Test, you will have to read and interpret information in time lines and diagrams. To answer questions based on these visuals, you will have to:

- determine the main idea of the time line or diagram
- read labels to understand the sequence of events in a time line
- read captions and labels to learn about an object or process in a diagram

The Civil War, Events of 1863

| Jan. | Feb. | Mar. | Apr. | May | June | July | Aug. | Sept. | Oct. | Nov. | Dec. |

Jan 1: Lincoln issues Emancipation Proclamation.

July 1-4: Union victories at Gettysburg and Vicksburg

July 13-16: Draft riots, NYC

Nov. 23: Union victory at Lookout Mountain

Sample Question

". . Now we are engaged in a great civil war, testing whether that nation, or any nation so conceived and so dedicated, can long endure. We are met on a great battlefield of that war. We have come to dedicate a portion of that field, as a final resting place for those who here gave their lives that that nation might live. It is altogether fitting and proper that we should do this. . . ."

—President Abraham Lincoln, Gettysburg, Pennsylvania, Nov. 19, 1863

Lincoln gave this speech just before which event on the time line?

(1) the Emancipation Proclamation
(2) the Battle of Gettysburg
(3) the Battle of Vicksburg
(4) the New York draft riots
(5) the Battle of Lookout Mountain

Think It Through

Q: What does the time line show?
A: It shows Civil War events of 1863.

Q: What is the question asking?
A: The question is asking when Lincoln delivered the Gettysburg Address, in relation to events shown on the time line.

Q: Which choice is the best?
A: Choice 1 took place in January, before the Gettysburg Address.
Choice 2 took place in July, before the Gettysburg Address.
Choice 3 took place in July, before the Gettysburg Address.
Choice 4 took place in July, before the Gettysburg Address.
Choice 5 took place four days after the Gettysburg address.

Answer and Explanation

(5) the Battle of Lookout Mountain This Union victory took place on November 23, four days after Lincoln's speech on November 19.

Guided Practice

Questions 1–3 are based on the time line and passage below. Use the hints to help you answer the questions. Explain why you chose each answer.

Events Leading Up to World War II

1937	1938	1939	1940	1941
Japan invades China.	Germany annexes Austria; Munich Conference at which France and Great Britain appease Germany by granting it territory in Czechoslovakia.	Germany attacks Poland; Great Britain and France declare war on Germany.	Germany invades Holland, Belgium, and France; Japan, Germany, and Italy become allies; Germany attacks Great Britain.	Germany invades Russia; Japan attacks Pearl Harbor; U.S. declares war on Japan; Germany declares war on U.S.

HINT: Check the events of each year to identify the correct answer.

1. Based on the time line, when did Great Britain and France make concessions to Germany, allowing it to take Czech land?

   (1) 1937
   (2) 1938
   (3) 1939
   (4) 1940
   (5) 1941

   Answer _____ is correct because _____

   _____

   _____

HINT: First find Germany's declaration of war against the United States on the time line. Then work backward to find the cause.

2. According to the time line, what was the immediate cause of Germany's declaration of war on the United States?

   (1) The United States opposed Germany's annexation of Austria in 1938.
   (2) The United States came to the aid of Poland in 1939.
   (3) The United States supported Great Britain's war efforts.
   (4) Japan bombed the U.S. naval base at Pearl Harbor, Hawaii, in 1941.
   (5) The United States declared war on Japan, a German ally.

   Answer _____ is correct because _____

   _____

   _____

Answers and explanations start on page 91.

Choose the <u>one best answer</u> to each question.

<u>Questions 1 and 2</u> refer to this diagram from a guide for voters.

Front View of Ballot Scanner

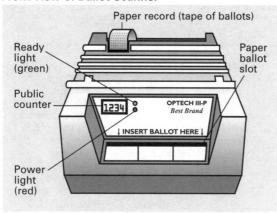

1. What is the purpose of this machine?

   THINK: Examine the diagram and read the title and labels carefully.

   (1) to register voters
   (2) to identify voters
   (3) to mark the ballots
   (4) to scan the ballots and tally votes
   (5) to record who has not yet voted

2. What is the tape for?

   THINK: Read the labels and think about the machine's purpose.

   (1) to provide music at the polls
   (2) to tell voters where to register
   (3) to record voting instructions
   (4) to tell voters where to sign the ballot
   (5) to produce a paper record of ballots cast

3. If the machine doesn't work properly, what might the board of electors do instead?

   THINK: How can you do this machine's job without it?

   (1) register voters by hand
   (2) require voters to show identification
   (3) mark each ballot by hand
   (4) use the paper record of ballots cast
   (5) count the votes by hand from the paper ballots

<u>Questions 4–6</u> refer to this information and diagram.

An economy goes through alternating periods of expansion and contraction. In the United States, a typical business cycle lasts about 12 years.

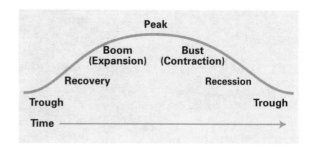

4. Which is the best title for this diagram?

   THINK: What does the diagram show?

   (1) Causes of Recession
   (2) Phases of the Business Cycle
   (3) How Economies Recover
   (4) Economic Expansion
   (5) A Peak Economy

5. Leslie wants to start her own business. At which point on the diagram above would it probably be best to start her business?

   THINK: In which type of economy would a new business be most likely to succeed?

   (1) recovery
   (2) peak
   (3) bust
   (4) recession
   (5) There is no good time for one person to start a business.

6. The business cycle influences employment. At which point on the diagram above would the unemployment rate be at its highest?

   THINK: In what type of economy would lots of people be out of work?

   (1) recovery
   (2) peak
   (3) bust
   (4) recession
   (5) trough

Questions 7 and 8 refer to the following information and diagram.

According to international law, the offshore areas of the ocean are divided into zones:

- The **territorial sea** belongs exclusively to the coastal nation.
- In the **contiguous zone,** the coastal nation can enforce its customs, immigration, and sanitation laws, but it doesn't own the area.
- In the **exclusive economic zone,** the coastal nation owns fishing and mineral rights.
- The **high seas,** or international waters, are open to all nations for any purpose.

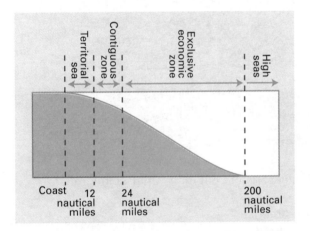

7. How close to shore can fishing ships of any nation fish without interference from the adjoining coastal nation?

   (1) up to the coast
   (2) 12 nautical miles
   (3) 24 nautical miles
   (4) 36 nautical miles
   (5) 200 nautical miles

8. There are many places where the zones don't work as shown above. Why not?

   (1) The coastline changes frequently.
   (2) The ocean floor slopes too sharply.
   (3) Nations are so close that zones overlap.
   (4) National law conflicts with international law.
   (5) International law doesn't apply.

Questions 9 and 10 refer to the following information and diagram.

One of the major functions of the executive branch's bureaucracy is to make and implement public policy. Also very influential in policy-making are congressional committees and special interest groups. The interaction in a particular policy area is called an iron triangle.

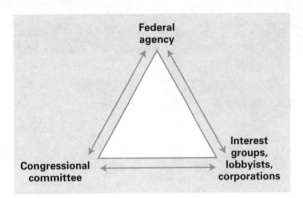

9. Which party in an iron triangle is from the legislative branch?

   (1) the federal agency
   (2) the interest groups
   (3) the congressional committee
   (4) lobbyists
   (5) corporations

10. Which of the following is an iron triangle?

   (1) The Cabinet, the House Armed Services Committee, and the Republican Party
   (2) The Department of State, the Department of Transportation, and the Department of Health
   (3) The Supreme Court, the Senate, and the National Organization of Women
   (4) The Department of Veterans Affairs, the House Committee on Veterans Affairs, and the Veterans of Foreign Wars
   (5) The Environmental Protection Agency, the House Subcommittee on Aging, and the National Council of Teachers of English.

Answers and explanations start on page 92.

Definition

Some questions on the GED Social Studies Test will be based on maps. To answer these questions you will have to:

● determine the main idea of the map
● read and interpret the map key and labels
● examine the relationships between places and data

World Migration, 1600–1900

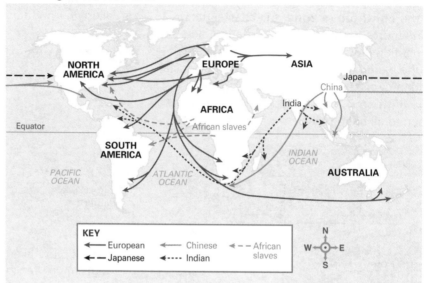

Sample Question

During the period the map shows, where did many Chinese migrate to?

(1) Europe, Africa, and North America
(2) Africa, North America, and Southeast Asia
(3) North America, Southeast Asia, and South America
(4) Southeast Asia, South America, and Australia
(5) South America, Australia, and Europe

Think It Through

Q: What does the map show?
A: The map shows world migration from 1600 to 1900.

Q: What is the question asking?
A: The question is asking to what areas the Chinese moved.

Q: Which choice is the correct answer?
A: Choice 1 is incorrect because the Chinese didn't move to Europe.
Choice 2 is correct because the Chinese moved to all three areas.
Choices 3 and 4 are incorrect because the Chinese didn't move to South America.
Choice 5 is wrong; the Chinese didn't move to Australia or Europe.

Answer and Explanation

(2) Africa, North America, and Southeast Asia Arrows indicating migration go from China to all three areas.

Guided Practice

<u>Questions 1 and 2</u> are based on the map below. Use the hints to help you answer the questions. Explain why you chose each answer.

The U.S. South, 1861

HINT: Check the map's key to find out how the second group of states to secede is represented.

1. Which states left the Union during the second wave of secession?

   (1) Missouri, Kentucky, West Virginia, Maryland, Delaware
   (2) Illinois, Indiana, Ohio
   (3) Arkansas, Tennessee, North Carolina, Virginia
   (4) South Carolina, Georgia, Florida, Alabama
   (5) Texas, Kansas, Iowa

   Answer _____ is correct because _____

   _____

   _____

HINT: Locate Washington, D.C., on the map. What would have been the effect on Washington if Maryland had seceded?

2. In 1861, Union soldiers were attacked in Baltimore, Maryland, by southern sympathizers. President Lincoln quickly jailed hundreds of secessionists, including many state legislators. As a result, Maryland stayed in the Union. Based on the map, why did Lincoln take such strong action?

   (1) Maryland was bordered by Delaware and Pennsylvania
   (2) Maryland was bordered by Virginia and West Virginia.
   (3) A large bay divided Maryland into two sections.
   (4) Washington, D.C., needed direct access to the Union states.
   (5) Washington, D.C., was closer to Maryland than to Ohio.

   Answer _____ is correct because _____

   _____

   _____

Answers and explanations start on page 92.

Choose the <u>one best answer</u> to each question.

Questions 1–3 refer to the following map.

Composition of U.S. Senate, 109th Congress, 2005

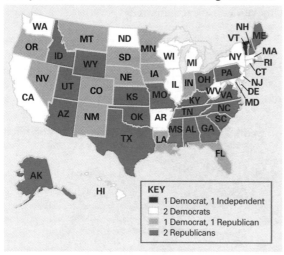

Questions 4–6 refer to the following map.

Per Capita Income in the United States, 2003

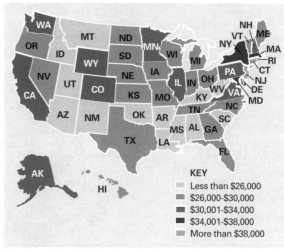

Source: U.S. Bureau of Economic Analysis

1. In 2005, from which political parties were the two senators from Illinois?

THINK: How is Illinois shown on the map? What does this mean, based on the map key?

(1) Both were Democrats.
(2) Both were Republicans.
(3) Both were Independents.
(4) One was a Democrat; one was a Republican.
(5) One was a Democrat; one was an Independent.

2. Which of these states had two Republican senators in 2005?

THINK: Study the map key; then look at the map.

(1) Colorado   **(3)** Maine   **(5)** Vermont
(2) Iowa   **(4)** Nevada

3. What data from the map <u>disproves</u> the generalization that in 2005, all southern states had at least one Republican senator?

THINK: Which southern state has two non-Republican senators?

(1) Ohio had two Republican senators.
(2) Florida had one Democratic senator.
(3) Louisiana had one Democratic senator.
(4) Arkansas had two Democratic senators.
(5) New Jersey had two Democratic senators.

4. Which of the following states had the lowest per capita (per person) income in 2003?

THINK: Check the map key to see how the lowest income is represented. Then find the state from this group with the lowest income.

(1) Colorado   **(4)** Nebraska
(2) Kansas   **(5)** Oklahoma
(3) Minnesota

5. Which of these states had the highest per capita income in 2003?

THINK: Check the map key against these states.

(1) Connecticut   **(4)** New York
(2) Michigan   **(5)** South Carolina
(3) New Hampshire

6. Which of the following people would find the information on this map most useful?

THINK: Who could use information on national variation in personal income levels?

(1) a party official planning a local political campaign
(2) a retiree deciding where to move
(3) a luxury retailer selecting the location for a new store
(4) a farmer planning next year's crops
(5) a tourist planning a cross-country trip

Questions 7–9 refer to this map.

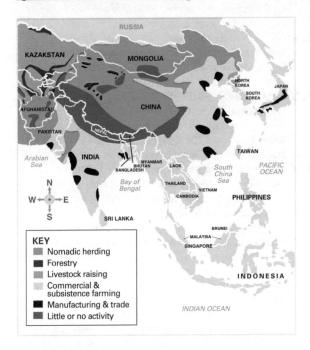

Question 10 refers to this paragraph and map.

In 1808, Emperor Napoleon Bonaparte of France overthrew the king of Spain. Napoleon had no interest in maintaining Spain's colonial power in the Americas. By 1836, the map of Central America and South America looked like this:

Central and South America, 1800–1836

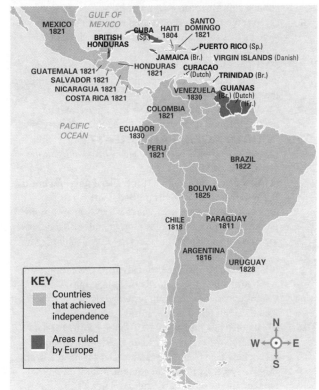

7. What is the best title for this map?

(1) Asia
(2) Asia: Land Use
(3) Asia: Sea Routes
(4) Asia: Climate Zones
(5) Asia: Elevation

8. Anna lives in a landlocked nation whose area is mostly given over to nomadic herding. Where does Anna live?

(1) China
(2) India
(3) Laos
(4) Mongolia
(5) Nepal

9. Which question can be answered by the information on this map?

(1) What is the capital of China?
(2) What is the longest river in India?
(3) Which nations have areas of little or no economic activity?
(4) What mountain ranges are located in Asia?
(5) What is the climate of Japan?

10. What is implied by the information in the paragraph and the map?

(1) Europe had little influence on events in the Western Hemisphere.
(2) Spain encouraged these nations to fight France for their independence.
(3) The United States helped the nations of Central and South America achieve independence.
(4) Most of the newly independent nations had been French colonies.
(5) Most of the newly independent nations had been Spanish colonies.

Answers and explanations start on page 92.

EARLY CIVILIZATIONS, PAGES 14–15

1. **(4) China** Silk production was a unique accomplishment of the Chinese.

2. **(2) Mesopotamia** The passage states Mesopotamia arose between these two rivers.

3. **(5) the Roman republic** Representative government was developed in Rome.

4. **(3) the Athenian assembly** All Athenian citizens could participate directly in the governing of their city-state, much like the participation in modern town meetings in some small American communities.

5. **(2) greater unity in the Roman Empire** Foreigners who were also citizens of Rome had a greater stake in the success of the empire.

6. **(5) An eye for an eye; a tooth for a tooth.** This saying expresses the idea that the punishment should be equal to the crime.

7. **(4) Aztec** According to the map key the Aztec civilization was flourishing when the Spanish arrived.

THE MIDDLE AGES, PAGES 16–17

1. **(2) Mali.** Timbuktu became a center of learning in the civilization of Mali.

2. **(1) Western Europe had decentralized government by feudal lords, and Byzantium had centralized authority in an emperor.** The Western Roman Empire fell apart into local fiefdoms after the fall of Rome, but the Eastern Roman Empire kept its central authority in Byzantium.

3. **(4) Afghanistan, where large areas of the countryside were controlled by warlords** In 2004, Afghanistan's central government had authority mainly in the capital Kabul, but in other areas warlords ruled.

4. **(5) Its officials and priests all spoke Latin.** The fact that church officials spoke Latin in addition to their native languages helped make it easier for people from different parts of Europe to communicate with one another and to share ideas and develop aspects of a common culture.

5. **(3) In which Crusade were the stated goals of the Church best met?** According to the chart, the First Crusade was the only one in which the stated goal of the Catholic Church was accomplished.

EUROPEAN EXPANSION, PAGES 18–19

1. **(3) to improve the Church from inside the organization** The Catholic Reformation was a reform movement led by people in the Church.

2. **(1) good trade routes to the Orient** The first European explorers were mostly concerned with finding good trade routes to India and China.

3. **(4) the selling of indulgences** If forgiveness of sins was based on faith rather than on actions, then buying indulgences, sold by the Church, would not affect whether a person was or was not forgiven for his or her sins.

4. **(5) the Internet** With the Internet, as with the printing press of Renaissance Europe, there was a sudden increase in the ease and speed at which information could be shared.

5. **(5) European colonizers** The paragraph focuses mainly on the motives and actions of Europeans involved in exploration and colonization in the 1400s and the 1500s.

6. **(2) to promote the image of Venice and attract business** The image glorifies the virtues of Venice, just as a modern-day ad for economic development of a city or state would.

REVOLUTIONS, PAGES 20–21

1. **(2) a period in the 1600s and 1700s in which observation and reason were applied to the study of human societies** The Enlightenment period in Europe is also sometimes called the Age of Reason.

2. **(3) Employment shifted from farms and homes to factories and cities.** Industrialization required people to work in large numbers in factories, which were increasingly located in cities.

3. **(1) The universe exists to provide a place for human beings.** An Earth-centered view of the universe is based on the assumption that humans are the most important species in the universe.

4. **(4) the abolition of slavery** Although the right to liberty was not at first thought to extend to slaves, eventually the idea was broadened to include all human beings.

5. **(5) Per person annual income doubled between 1760 and 1860.** Income rose from $399 to $804 during these years of the Industrial Revolution.

THE TWENTIETH CENTURY, PAGES 22–23

1. **(3) the Caribbean, Central America, and the Philippines** The passage states that these were all areas of U.S. control during the Age of Imperialism.

2. **(2) Great Britain controlled trading rights in the Yangtze River Valley and at the port of Shanghai in China.** Control of economic activity and trade was characteristic of a sphere of influence.

3. **(1) the German invasion of Poland** This was the event that caused Great Britain and France to declare war on Germany, eventually drawing many other nations to declare war.

4. **(1) Italy** The passage states that Italy allied itself with Germany during World War II.

5. **(4) Both nations saw an opportunity to gain influence and allies worldwide.** Each nation was seeking to expand and consolidate its global power during the postwar period.

6. **(3) The German leader writes "I'm broke."** After World War I, the defeated Germany was expected to pay all the war damages—an impossible task for one nation.

THE AMERICAN COLONIES, PAGES 24–25

1. **(1) Spain** With the gold and other precious metals the Spanish mined in their American colonies, Spain became the world's wealthiest nation in the 1500s.

2. **(4) fur trading** The French were more interested in trading with the Indians than in establishing large settlements in the New World.

3. **(5) Maryland** Pennsylvania was founded in part to provide religious freedom for Quakers; Maryland was founded in part to provide religious freedom for Catholics.

4. **(1) democratic political institutions** The passage describes three English colonies that had constitutions and/or legislatures, both of which are important components of democratic political institutions.

5. **(3) The population grew slowly.** Malaria and yellow fever took a toll on the early Carolina settlers, keeping the population low.

6. **(3) A society needs rules to prosper.** The Mayflower Compact set out rules for government, implying that the signers believed that rules were needed to help their new colony, which was their society, function at its best.

7. **(3) 746,000** Find the entry for Spanish South America and read across.

8. **(2) To which region in the Americas were most slaves brought?** This question can be answered by looking at the chart. The West Indies imported the greatest number of slaves.

THE AMERICAN REVOLUTION, PAGES 26–27

1. **(2) It needed to protect its North American empire and to tax the colonists to pay for wars.** Great Britain wanted the colonies to bear more of the financial burden for their upkeep.

2. **(3) the Declaration of Independence** The document's name and the commitment of the colonies to fighting in the American Revolution both indicate that this document announced the colonial break from British rule.

3. **(3) boycotting British goods** Colonial boycotts led to the repeal of the Stamp Act and the Townshend Acts.

4. **(1) A government can rule only with the consent of the governed.** The colonists had no representatives in Parliament. They considered taxes that Parliament levied against them to be a violation of this general principle of government.

5. **(4) It formed an army to fight Britain and also petitioned the king to restore rights.** The Second Continental Congress took actions to satisfy its rebellious as well as loyal delegates.

6. **(4) 3** Find the wedge labeled Doctors; read the number.

7. **(1) More than half of the framers were lawyers.** The total number of delegates was 55; adding the number of lawyers (9) plus the number of lawyers who also farmed (18) plus the number of lawyers who were public officials (4) gives 31, which is more than half the total, (55). You can determine this is more than half the total because the wedges representing members who were lawyers take up more than half the circle graph.

EXPANSION AND CIVIL WAR, PAGES 28–29

1. **(1) The Louisiana Purchase, 1803** This acquisition roughly doubled the size of the original territory of the United States (the thirteen colonies and the territory ceded by Britain in 1783).

2. **(5) Westward Expansion of the United States to 1860** This title is the best because it describes the content of the map without being too general or too specific.

3. **(4) Senators usually voted along regional lines, and admitting Missouri would have given the South a majority by two votes.** The admission of Missouri as a slave state would have meant 12 slave states and 11 free states. Since there are two senators from each state, that would have given the South a majority by two votes.

4. **(2) the annexation of Texas in 1845** This acquisition from Mexico was part of the westward expansion of the United States.

5. **(1) It was the first step the U.S. government took to abolish slavery.** The Emancipation Proclamation was the first time the U.S. government passed any laws to abolish slavery.

6. **(4) Civil War soldiers had more to fear from illness, malnutrition, and exposure than from combat.** About 375,000 soldiers died from disease and other causes compared with about 185,000 who died in combat.

INDUSTRIALIZATION AND IMMIGRATION, PAGES 30–31

1. **(2) the formation of trusts to decrease competition** The passage implies that control of all aspects of an industry by a single business contributed the most to industrial growth.

2. **(1) southern and eastern Europe** This was in contrast to earlier immigration, which was mostly from northern Europe.

3. **(2) Andrew Carnegie, a poor Scottish immigrant who became a steel tycoon in Pennsylvania** Andrew Carnegie's spectacular rise to the head of the steel industry was often cited as a true source of American rags-to-riches stories.

4. **(2) The trusts lobbied for a weakened bill.** The trusts were influential in Washington, D. C. and early on were able to weaken intended reforms.

5. **(3) by showing individual faces of the soldiers to humanize them** The drawing is made from the point of view of the soldiers in the foreground, who are depicted as individuals, several of whom have calm, steady expressions. The workers, on the other hand, are a faceless mob in the distance.

WORLD POWER, PAGES 32–33

1. **(5) Germany torpedoed ocean liners, killing several hundred U.S. passengers.** The unrestricted submarine warfare of Germany forced the U.S. to get involved in the war.

2. **(1) the United Nations, an international peacekeeping organization** Both organizations had the same goals and each grew out of a world war.

3. **(4) the extremely high unemployment rate** According to the passage, unemployment reached 25 percent in 1932, a relatively large proportion of the population.

4. **(5) commitment to different economic and political systems** The Cold War resulted because of disagreements about the spread of communism—a political and economic system embraced by the Soviet Union and opposed by the United States.

5. **(4) the sole superpower** When the Soviet Union collapsed in 1991, the U.S. remained as the only superpower.

6. **(3) Coalition forces went only as far as the Euphrates River.** The coalition did not push on to Baghdad, the capital, to unseat Saddam Hussein.

THE BRANCHES OF GOVERNMENT, PAGES 34–35

1. **(5) controlling the federal budget** According to the passage, Congress has the power to tax and spend, which enables it to control budget policy.
2. **(3) Having job security protects judges from political pressure when making rulings.** This is one way to check the power of the legislative and executive branches.
3. **(2) the right to make treaties with other nations** Negotiating agreements with foreign nations is one of the president's powers.
4. **(1) the abuse of power** The separation of powers among the branches of government helps check the human tendency to try to amass more and more power.
5. **(3) The Rules Committee decides which bills go to the full House.** The diagram indicates that the Rules Committee can put a bill on the calendar for debate in the full House, or not.
6. **(5) Most bills never become law.** The diagram shows a number of stages. A bill can be rejected at any stage.

THE U.S. CONSTITUTION, PAGES 36–37

1. **(3) to regulate in-state commerce** According to the chart, only the states can regulate commerce within their borders.
2. **(1) to protect the rights of ordinary citizens** The Bill of Rights outlines citizens' rights and liberties.
3. **(4) to place a check on the power of the national government** By giving some powers to the states, the Constitution decreases the power of the federal government.
4. **(4) establishing a process for becoming a citizen** The federal government has the power to regulate immigration and naturalization.
5. **(2) the Second Amendment** The Second Amendment protects the right to bear arms (weapons).
6. **(4) Texas** The number of executions is given next to or under the state abbreviation. According to the map, Texas had 23 executions in 2004.
7. **(5) Does federal law require the death penalty for violent crimes?** If there were a federal law requiring the death penalty for any crime, the map would not have the category "States with No Death Penalty." That is because federal law always supersedes state law. Therefore, the map allows you to answer the question, indicating that "No" is the answer.

ELECTIONS, PAGES 38–39

1. **(2) to get its candidates elected** Political parties seek to influence public policy through political office. Therefore, their main goal is to elect as many of their politicians as possible.
2. **(2) by lobbying** Lobbying is the chief activity of most special interest groups.
3. **(3) the local Republican Party** Since the brochure was advertising all the Republican candidates for city council, it most likely came from the local Republican party rather than from a particular candidate.
4. **(5) a practical approach to getting elected** Politicians, especially those up for election, try to appeal to as wide a range of voters as possible.

5. **(3) any party other than the Democrats or Republicans** This is implied in the third paragraph of the passage.
6. **(3) They both serve as ways to link the citizen with the government.** Both are ways for citizens to participate in politics.
7. **(4) From 1975 to 2004, the number of Democratic governors fell and the number of Republican governors rose.** Overall, the Democratic trend line goes down, and the Republican trend line goes up, during this period.

CITIZENS' RIGHTS AND RESPONSIBILITIES, PAGES 40–41

1. **(5) the right to vote** According to the Supreme Court, all other political rights depend on this right.
2. **(1) a resident alien** Most states reserve voting for citizens.
3. **(4) the Nineteenth and Twenty-Sixth** The Nineteenth Amendment gave the vote to women; the Twenty-Sixth gave the vote to 18-year-olds.
4. **(1) Recruitment and reenlistment figures drop during protracted warfare.** Declining enrollment means possible shortfalls in military personnel that a draft could solve.
5. **(4) equal rights for all** Gradually the vote was extended to all men (including former slaves), to women, and to the young.
6. **(3) a nonvoter** The man responds the pollster's question about reasons for low voter turnout with both ignorance ("I don't know") and apathy ("I don't care"). This indicates that the man falls into the category of citizen the pollster is asking about: nonvoters.
7. **(2) citizens' lack of knowledge about and interest in politics** The cartoonist attributes low turnout to the attitude of the typical nonvoting citizen, who doesn't follow political news and doesn't care about politics.

THE U.S. ECONOMY, PAGES 42–43

1. **(1) a web of transactions between buyers and sellers** The passage states that a market is a network of buying and selling.
2. **(3) to make a profit** The passage indicates that the desire to make money is the main incentive for risk-taking and working in a market economy.
3. **(2) The price of DVD players will fall.** When there are too many DVD players, manufacturers and/or merchants lower the price in order to sell them.
4. **(5) a need for order and control** A centrally directed economy concentrates authority in government agencies, which seek orderly economic activity through central planning.
5. **(5) as a mixed economy** The passage states that the U.S. economy combines a market economy with government regulation.
6. **(4) clothing** Among the choices, clothing is the only product; the rest are services.
7. **(2) 20,000** The demand curve indicates how many bags of potato chips consumers are likely to buy at a certain price. Find $3.00 on that curve and read down to the x-axis. The number is 20,000.
8. **(2) $2.00** According to the definition, the equilibrium price is the price at which supply equals demand. This is the point on the graph where the demand curve intersects the supply curve. Find that point and then read across to the y-axis to find the price: $2.00.

ECONOMICS AND GOVERNMENT, PAGES 44–45

1.   **(3) It is not practical for individuals or companies to produce or obtain them.** Public goods need to be available to all. Producing them usually wouldn't give companies a profit, so private business has no incentive to produce them.

2.   **(2) alternating periods of economic expansion and contraction** The passage indicates that the business cycle consists of boom times and recessions.

3.   **(1) lowering the discount rate** When the Fed lowers the discount rate, it becomes cheaper to borrow money to finance business expansion.

4.   **(1) Occupational Safety and Health Administration** This agency's mission is to set workplace standards for worker health and safety.

5.   **(4) Fiscal policy takes longer to put into action than monetary policy.** Since fiscal policy involves cooperation between the president and Congress, as well as the passage of laws involving spending, it takes longer to implement than monetary policy, which is set by the Federal Reserve Board at its monthly meetings.

6.   **(4) about one-half** The portion of the circle graph that represents payments to individuals occupies half of the circle ($1,041 billion of a total budget of $2,081 billion).

WORKERS AND CONSUMERS, PAGES 46–47

1.   **(3) the price paid for labor** Wages are the money paid to workers for their services.

2.   **(2) money loaned to consumers to purchase items** According to the passage, money can be loaned for specific purchases (such as cars) or through credit cards.

3.   **(4) Consumer demand for goods and services will fall.** When workers are unemployed, they have less money to spend, so demand for goods and services decreases.

4.   **(1) iron ore** Iron ore is a natural resource, so it is classified by economists as land.

5.   **(1) cheap labor** The passage states that many owners of textile factories have moved their factories to Mexico to take advantage of the large supply of cheap labor there.

6.   **(5) the give and take of compromise** With most contracts, neither the labor union nor management can get everything they want; they must be willing to compromise to negotiate successfully.

7.   **(4) to persuade consumers to buy gift bags at Deep Discount Stores** The ad headline indicates that the ad is from Deep Discount Stores. For each size bag, the ad compares the higher price at a competing chain, ABC Stores, to the lower price at Deep Discount in order to convince consumers to buy the bags at Deep Discount.

WORLD REGIONS, PAGES 48–49

1.   **(3) World Climate Zones** The map is of the world, and it shows the distribution of climate regions.

2.   **(4) What type of climate does North Africa have?** The map shows climate zones of the world. Note that the map shows that North Africa has a desert climate.

3.   **(3) climate, vegetation, and animal life** These three factors together determine the characteristics of biome.

4.   **(5) tundra** No trees, low vegetation, and permafrost are all characteristic of the tundra biome.

5.   **(1) steppe** Cattle graze on grass. The map on page 48 indicates that the region is temperate. Temperate grassland is known as the steppe biome.

6.   **(2) desert** Continued decreased rainfall and plant life will turn a savannah into a desert.

7.   **(1) cotton** According to the chart, each of the nations in Central Asia produces cotton.

8.   **(3) Tajikistan because it relies solely on cotton and textiles** The chart shows that, unlike other the other nations listed, Tajikistan's economy is based on cotton and textiles alone. Problems with the cotton crop or decreased demand for textiles would harm Tajikistan's economy, and there would be few other activities for the country to fall back on.

CULTURES, PAGES 50–51

1.   **(1) universal categories of traits** These traits that all cultures have include religion, language, arts, and so on.

2.   **(3) the changing and spreading of a culture or cultural trait** The passage indicates that cultural diffusion involves change and distribution.

3.   **(1) English favored no particular ethnic group and provided a means of communication that everyone could use.** English became a common language; its adoption by the government prevented any one group from having a language advantage in the new nation.

4.   **(2) cultural diffusion through migration** The Spanish migrated from Europe and Mexico to the American Southwest, bringing their culture with them.

5.   **(5) Which Central American nation has the largest percentage of immigrants?** This question can be answered by comparing the percentages in the fourth column of the table.

RESOURCES, PAGES 52–53

1.   **(2) land, water, and air** All the other resources are derived from these three.

2.   **(4) Farms in southern California need water, but the north gets the most rain.** According to the passage, rain falls in the north, while southern California, with its agriculture and large population, is a dry region.

3.   **(4) fossil fuels** The factories of the Industrial Revolution increased the need for fossil fuels, especially coal. Before the Industrial Revolution, fossil fuels were much less important.

4.   **(2) Their political and economic power would decrease.** Since their power is based on the possession of oil, if oil became less important, Middle Eastern nations would lose some of their economic and political power.

5.   **(1) the economic value of each resource** In the United States, many decisions related to resource use have an economic basis. The exploited resource has more economic value than the affected resource, otherwise Americans would not sacrifice the affected resource.

6.   **(2) on the Dnepr River** The map key indicates that hydroelectric power is represented by the letter H. The symbol is found next to the Dneper River.

7.   **(2) No, it has many fossil fuel deposits.** Nations that lack fossil fuels are most likely to work to develop alternative energy sources.

COMPREHENSION QUESTIONS, PAGES 54–57
GUIDED PRACTICE, PAGE 55

1. **Answer (3)** is correct because the passage explains how the United States bought Louisiana Territory.
2. **Answer (2)** is correct. Jefferson sought to aid farmers who sold goods through the port of New Orleans by offering to buy the city from France.
3. **Answer (5)** is correct because events in Haiti discouraged France from trying to hold on to and administer its possessions in North America.

GED SKILL BUILDER PRACTICE 1, PAGES 56–57

1. **(5) Congress cannot override a pocket veto.** By the time the veto occurs, Congress is no longer in session.
2. **(3) The Role of Information in Consumer Choices** The paragraph explains how information helps consumers make wise buying decisions.
3. **(4) 1,800 m³** Locate the bar that is labeled "United States." From the top of the bar, read across to the vertical axis to find the amount of water, listed in cubic meters.
4. **(5) Canadians and Americans use about twice as much water per person as Mexicans do.** This summary covers all the main information presented by the graph.
5. **(4) He did not call Parliament into session for long periods of time.** Whenever Parliament challenged Charles, he shut it down for years.
6. **(5) Causes of the English Civil War** The passage describes events that led to the English Civil War.
7. **(1) The king has absolute power.** If a king's power is divine, or comes from God, he can do whatever he thinks is right.
8. **(2) Young children as well as parents contributed to the family income.** The photo shows the entire family working together.

APPLICATION QUESTIONS, PAGES 58–61
GUIDED PRACTICE, PAGE 59

1. **Answer (3)** is correct because like Best Corp., the couple is borrowing money to buy a building.
2. **Answer (1)** is correct because the cheese maker is changing a raw material (milk) into a value-added product (cheese).

GED SKILL BUILDER PRACTICE 2, PAGES 60–61

1. **(1) the present African AIDS epidemic, which has killed thousands of adults and orphaned their children** This epidemic is causing widespread social and economic dislocations in Africa.
2. **(1) the National Coalition for Disability Rights defending the right of disabled Americans to fair and equal treatment** This is another example of a group pressing for equal rights under the law.
3. **(2) a criminal trial, because murder is a crime and California was the plaintiff** Murder is a violation of the criminal code, and the government brought charges against Simpson, making this a criminal trial.

4. **(4) a civil trial, because it was a matter between private individuals** Both parties to the suit were individuals, so this was a civil trial.
5. **(3) cigarette tax** This is a sin tax because it's a tax on a specific product that the government is trying to decrease consumption of.
6. **(1) agricultural potential** The Spanish chose the location because they could farm there.
7. **(3) head of navigation** Boats can travel upriver to Trenton, so river trade and transport is possible.
8. **(5) defense** Being surrounded by water made the first area of Paris that was settled easily defensible. (The city eventually grew much larger, spreading to both banks of the river and beyond.)
9. **(4) confluence of two rivers** Pittsburgh is sited where two rivers meet.
10. **(2) a French fast-food chain becoming established in the United States** Both focus on the globalization of large restaurant chains.

ANALYSIS QUESTIONS, PAGES 62–65
GUIDED PRACTICE, PAGE 63

1. **Answer (2)** is correct because the Court viewed slaves as property rather than as citizens with rights.
2. **Answer (4)** is correct because the North would oppose anything giving the South more power, and the South would favor it.

GED SKILL BUILDER PRACTICE 3, PAGES 64–65

1. **(3) Other firms would enter the industry.** If other firms had access to bauxite, they would be more likely go into the aluminum business.
2. **(2) Agriculture is difficult, and food must be imported.** The arid and semiarid climate of Namibia makes it very hard to grow enough food to feed the country.
3. **(5) Leopold is squeezing the man.** Leopold is represented as a snake whose coils are crushing the population of the Congo, represented by the man.
4. **(5) Wilson was a gifted leader who did the right thing by entering World War I.** This statement is a belief rather than a fact that can be proved true.
5. **(1) The later interpretation is much more favorable to Wilson.** The later interpretation treats Wilson's actions as inevitable and as motivated by the good of the nation.
6. **(1) Make registration more convenient.** Since the most people gave not being registered as their reason for not voting, the chart indicates that making registration easier is most likely to improve voter turnout.
7. **(4) They are typically very small.** Because a sole proprietorship involves the work of one person, these businesses have relatively low sales.

EVALUATION QUESTIONS, PAGES 66–69
GUIDED PRACTICE, PAGE 67

1. **Answer (4)** is correct. The passage indicates that Europeans under Napoleon resented foreign rule and wanted to restore their own governments and ways of life. This shows they valued their national identity.
2. **Answer (5)** is correct because decreasing international trade means decreased economic activity, a further contraction of the economy.

GED SKILL BUILDER PRACTICE 4, PAGES 68–69

1. **(1) openness in government proceedings** Public trials help protect the individual against government abuses of power.

2. **(1) Criminal trials should be televised.** A televised trial is very public.

3. **(3) the welfare of ordinary people** Based on the groups the Progressives opposed, you can infer that the Progressives placed a high value on the welfare of ordinary people.

4. **(3) When did the government have a budget surplus?** This can be answered by looking at the shaded surplus area and checking the dates on the horizontal axis.

5. **(1) the difference between receipts and spending that year** Spending was more than receipts in 2004, so there was a deficit.

6. **(1) Which countries border Colombia?** This is a political map, which shows boundaries between countries.

7. **(5) In the political world, as in nature, only the strongest survive.** This idea was used by the colonial powers to justify their domination of weaker peoples.

8. **(2) Personal diplomacy would help solve international problems.** By setting up the hotline, the leaders indicated they believed they could resolve crises with direct personal contact, i.e., personal diplomacy.

9. **(3) How did President Kennedy counter the threat of missiles in Cuba?** According to the passage, Kennedy blockaded Cuba.

GRAPHS AND CHARTS, PAGES 70–73 GUIDED PRACTICE, PAGE 71

1. **Answer (1)** is correct. The second set of bars indicates income for families in which both the husband and wife have jobs; the second bar is represents the yearly family income for 2000.

2. **Answer (4)** is correct. Average yearly income is least when there is no husband present and just the wife is working.

GED SKILL BUILDER PRACTICE 5, PAGES 72–73

1. **(1) Roman Catholicism** According to the chart, Roman Catholics make up 84.1% of the population.

2. **(3) its location in the typhoon belt** According to the chart, the Philippines is hit by an average of six typhoons (hurricanes) per year. Typhoons often result in loss of life and property damage, making them weather disasters.

3. **(2) national newspapers** According to the graph, only 7% of respondents got their news from a national newspaper.

4. **(1) national broadcast TV** Reaching 36% of Americans, of the sources listed, this medium would get Janice the largest national audience.

5. **(3) 12%** On the Massachusetts graph, locate the wedge representing artists and craftspeople. The figure is 12%.

6. **(5) small farmer** Look for the wedge on the Virginia circle graph that makes up just under 20% of the graph; it is the wedge representing small farmers, at 19.8%.

7. **(3) the percentage of large landowners in Virginia compared to the percentage in Massachusetts** The Massachusetts assembly had no large plantation owners, whereas more than one-third of the Virginia assembly were large landowners.

8. **(4) the Americas, because their population fell between 1000 and 1700 and then rose** None of the other regions experienced a decrease in population at any of the time intervals that are shown in the table.

EDITORIAL CARTOONS AND PHOTOGRAPHS, PAGES 74–77 GUIDED PRACTICE, PAGE 75

1. **Answer (5)** is correct because the photo shows a row of men in front of the anti-suffragist headquarters.

2. **Answer (3)** is correct because anti-suffragists thought women should focus on home life and that they did not need to have a voice in politics.

GED SKILL BUILDER PRACTICE 6, PAGES 76–77

1. **(3) Congress** This is written on the Jolly Green Giant's chest.

2. **(2) The Jolly Green Giant is tossing money for the farmer to catch.** The farmer is getting "free money" according to the cartoonist.

3. **(3) demonstrating for a cause** From the large group and the signs, you can tell this is a demonstration. No candidate names are shown, so you can infer that the demonstration is for a cause.

4. **(1) What group of people is in the photo?** The placard shows that the photo is of a group of union sheet metal workers.

5. **(4) The Germans favored the destruction of the Wall, and the Soviets opposed it.** In the photo, the Germans are atop the Wall in triumph; note the man holding his arms up and signaling "V" for victory. You can infer that the Soviets opposed the destruction of the Berlin Wall, even if they didn't try to stop it. It meant a loss of power and prestige for them.

6. **(2) The United States has an imperial interest in Latin America.** Uncle Sam is asserting his influence over Latin America in this cartoon.

TIME LINES AND DIAGRAMS, PAGES 78–81 GUIDED PRACTICE, PAGE 79

1. **Answer (2)** is correct because the concessions were made at the Munich Conference in 1938.

2. **Answer (5)** is correct; the time line indicates that Germany and Japan became allies in 1940 and that the German declaration came after the United States declared war on Japan as a result of the Japanese attack on Pearl Harbor, in 1941.

GED SKILL BUILDER PRACTICE 7, PAGES 80–81

1. **(4) to scan the ballots and tally votes** The title of the diagram indicates it is a ballot scanner.

2. **(5) to produce a paper record of ballots cast** As each ballot is scanned, it is recorded on the paper tape that comes out of the machine.

3. **(5) count the votes by hand from the paper ballots** If the scanners malfunction, the votes can be tallied by examining the paper ballots manually.

4. **(2) Phases of the Business Cycle** The diagram shows a complete business cycle from beginning to end.

5. **(1) recovery** Starting a business during a recovery would give the business time to become established as economic activity is growing.

6. **(5) trough** The low point of an economic cycle is characterized by very high unemployment.

7. **(5) 200 nautical miles** Foreign fishing boats must stay out of a nation's exclusive economic zone (200 nautical miles from shore).

8. **(3) Nations are so close that zones overlap.** This occurs, for example, wherever nations face one another across straits, as Cuba and the United States. In these cases, the zones must be negotiated.

9. **(3) the congressional committee** Congress is part of the legislative branch.

10. **(4) The Department of Veterans Affairs, the House Committee on Veterans Affairs, and the Veterans of Foreign Wars.** The Department of Veterans Affairs is a federal agency. The House Committee is part of Congress. The Veterans of Foreign Wars is a special interest group. All work together on veterans' issues.

MAPS, PAGES 82–85
GUIDED PRACTICE, PAGE 83

1. **Answer (3)** is correct because the map shows these states seceding in April and May 1861, the second group to secede.

2. **Answer (4)** is correct because if Maryland had seceded, Washington, D.C., would have been cut off from the free states in the North.

GED SKILL BUILDER PRACTICE 8, PAGES 84–85

1. **(1) Both were Democrats.** Illinois is shown in white, which according to the key means it had two Democratic senators in 2005.

2. **(3) Maine** Maine is the only state listed shown in gray, which indicates that it had two Republican senators in 2005.

3. **(4) Arkansas had two Democratic senators.** Arkansas was the only southern state with no Republican senator in 2005.

4. **(5) Oklahoma** Oklahoma is shown in light blue, which indicates in 2003, it was among states with the lowest per capita income.

5. **(1) Connecticut** Connecticut is shown in gray, which indicates in 2003, it was among states with the highest per capita income.

6. **(3) a luxury retailer selecting the location for a new store** Luxury retailers want to be located where incomes are high.

7. **(2) Asia: Land Use** The map shows the ways land is used in Asia.

8. **(4) Mongolia** Look on the key for nomadic herding, then find a country without a coastline that is mostly given over to it.

9. **(3) Which nations have areas of little or no economic activity?** The map shows areas of little or no economic activity in India, Nepal, Bhutan, China, and so on. Many of these areas are very mountainous.

10. **(5) Most of the newly independent nations had been Spanish colonies.** The map indicates that most nations in the region became independent between 1808 and 1836, when Napoleon held control of Spain. As the passage states, Napoleon had little interest in maintaining Spain's power in the Americas; you can infer that these nations gained independence partly due to the lack of control exerted over them by Napoleon and by Spain.